CONTENTS

ACKNOWLEDGEMENTS

The author wishes to acknowledge the following sources of material and help in the preparation of this Part:

J. A. Rogers, *Hydraulic and Pneumatic Power Journal*

R. Hey, *Hydraulic and Air Engineering Journal*

H. W. Marks, Publicity Manager, Keelavite Hydraulics Ltd.

J. L. Rye, Technical Training Officer, Keelavite Hydraulics Ltd.

J. A. Burton, Senior Applications Engineer, Lucas Industrial Equipment Ltd.

Adan Ltd.

Andrew Fraser Ltd.

Chamberlain Industries Ltd.

Fairey Filtration Ltd.

Fawcett Engineering Ltd.

Hägglund und Söner AB

Hamworthy Engineering Ltd.

Hydraulics and Pneumatics Ltd.

Keelavite Hydraulics Ltd.

K & L Marine Equipment Ltd.

Lucas Industrial Equipment Ltd.

Sperry-Vickers Ltd.

Stothert and Pitt Ltd.

Vickers Ltd.

Weir Pumps Ltd.

INTRODUCTION

The transmission of power by some form of hydraulic drive is well established in every field of engineering and some of the earliest equipment produced was for marine applications.

In fact, positive displacement piston pumps and motors, specifically for use in marine power transmission with oil, were produced about 1800.

It is a testimony to the design of several of these products that equipment which is still generally similar continues to be used today, although the obvious improvements in materials and manufacturing techniques have, in most cases, allowed performance ratings to be increased.

From these beginnings, the employment of hydraulics has grown until the range of equipment available today is wide and the applications are numerous and varied; in some cases, hydraulic systems are used as an alternative to electrical drives, but in other applications they constitute the optimum choice for the task in hand.

The choice of the drive method depends upon many factors and can involve tradition, environment, safety and cost. Perhaps this is not the place to continue the argument, but suffice it to say that the debate continues along with the progressive development of equipment and the increasing demands of modern engineering systems.

As well as considering the specific equipment in use in modern ships and the criteria governing the design and maintenance of hydraulic systems, a few fundamental concepts regarding fluid power are reviewed and some elementary mathematical equations are presented describing the main parameters of any system, i.e. flow pressure, torque, speed, power, etc.

In this way it is hoped that a reasonably comprehensive, if brief, coverage of the topic has been achieved.

1. PRINCIPLES OF HYDRAULIC
POWER TRANSMISSION

1.1. HYDROSTATIC HYDRAULIC POWER TRANSMISSION

By definition, power transmission involves energy transfer from point to point and this can be achieved hydraulically through two fundamental processes. In the first, energy is transferred by conversion into momentum in the mass of oil—moving a relatively large volume at high velocity—and then re-converting this momentum at a working interface. This *hydrokinetic* process is achieved in fluid couplings or torque convertors which are used as elements in a straight line power shaft system to achieve a shock absorbing or smooth speed change, or to provide torque variation. The basic elements of turbine and impellor can be arranged to either produce a direct speed ratio approaching 1:1 (i.e. no speed change other than efficiency losses), or to produce an automatic speed/torque change by using a third reacting member. In either case, power and speed conversion is achieved within the single "coupling" containing turbine and impellor.

Fluid couplings of either type have a relatively narrow field of application compared to fluid power in general and so will not be considered further.

The second process is generally referred to as being *hydrostatic*. In this process, mechanical energy (force and velocity) is converted into fluid pressure and flow in a pumping mechanism and re-converted into either linear or rotary motion at the work station. The conversion of mechanical to hydraulic power (pump) can be sited at considerable distance from the work station (motor or cylinder). Fluid velocities are relatively low, but pressures are high compared to those in the hydrokinetic process. The working fluid (usually a high quality mineral oil) circulates from pump to motor or cylinder through hydraulic pipelines which are designed to withstand the fluid pressures involved.

1.2. THE ADVANTAGES OF HYDRAULICS

Many reasons can be suggested for the use of hydraulic systems in marine engineering:

   a) A convenient method of transferring power over relatively long distances from, say, a central pump room to remote operating sites in the ship; where necessary, complete local control of operations can be achieved;

b) Fully variable speed control of both linear and rotary motion, with good "inching" capability and smooth take up of load; in all cases power is continuously transmitted whilst speed changes take place;

c) High static forces or torques can be achieved and maintained indefinitely;

d) Complete safety and reliability is assured under the most difficult environmental conditions; overload conditions are safeguarded by using a relief valve to limit maximum output torques or forces;

e) Significant cost savings can be shown over alternative solutions for many requirements.

1.3. BASIC EQUIPMENT AND CIRCUITS

In practical terms, five main categories of equipment can be defined in order to achieve this power transmission:

1) The hydraulic pump to convert mechanical into hydraulic energy;

2) Valves to allow this hydraulic energy to be controlled;

3) Hydraulic cylinders to convert the hydraulic energy into linear force and motion (semi-rotary actuators achieve part rotation);

4) Hydraulic motors to convert the hydraulic energy into continuous rotary motion;

5) Ancillary equipment including filters, heat exchangers, tanks, pipes, etc. to complete practical circuits.

Although systems are designed to suit particular applications, basic circuits can be identified which illustrate the main principles and alternative types. These circuits are illustrated in Figs 1(a), (b), (c) and (d).

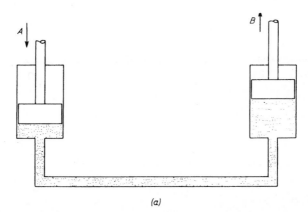

(a)

FIG. 1(a).—*Simplest hydraulic circuit. Oil line connects two cylinders. Movement of cylinder A causes corresponding movement in B. Working medium oscillates in pipeline.*

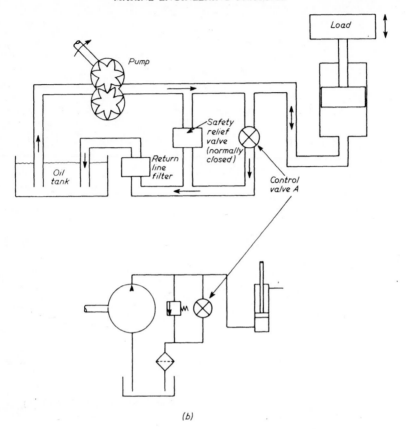

(b)

FIG. 1(b).—*Open circuit—linear output (fixed capacity pump). Oil circulates from pump through valve A back to tank. If valve A is closed, oil feed lifts load.*

1.4. SOME PARTICULAR FEATURES

Following on from the introduction of the principal circuit types, particular fundamental features of hydraulic power transmission can be identified before the practical equipment is described. These features play an important part in the design considerations of any circuit and the choice of equipment in that circuit.

1.4.1. Speed Ratio

As shown in Fig. 1(b), the operating speed of the cylinder is dependent upon the rate at which oil is supplied. With the pump running at a constant speed and driven by an electric motor, and considering control valve A as a simple switch initially (i.e. either fully open or fully closed), it is clear that with the valve open any resistance from the load will prevent movement and the oil from the pump will circulate directly back to tank.

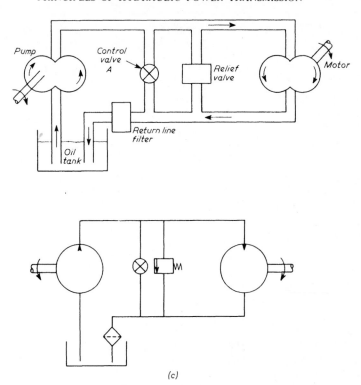

FIG. 1(c).—*Open circuit—rotary output (fixed capacity pump). Equivalent to circuit (b), but using a hydraulic motor to achieve continuous rotary drive.*

However, when valve A is closed, all the oil from the pump enters the cylinder and the rate of movement depends on the oil flow (pump size and speed) and cylinder capacity (vol/in). A larger pump flow, or a smaller diameter cylinder will increase speed. A smaller pump flow or a larger diameter cylinder will decrease output speed.

1.4.2. System Pressure, Force, and Power

In the situation shown in Fig. 1(b), the oil pressure at the pump when the load is moving is determined by the load and cylinder area. A smaller cylinder with the same pump will increase the rate at which the load will rise, but a higher oil pressure will be required. This will increase the required electric motor rating since the higher pressure and the same flow—a higher lift speed with the same load—will demand a higher power.

Maximum force available from the cylinder is given by the maximum system pressure (set by the safety relief valve) and the area of the ram.

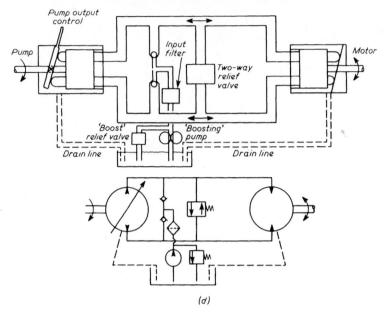

(d)

FIG. 1(d).—*Closed circuit—rotary output (variable capacity pump). Continuous rotary drive using variable capacity pump to achieve speed variations without control valve A. "Closed" circuit recirculates oil directly from motor to pump. Boosting pump keeps circuit charged with oil.*

1.4.3. Variable Speed

Referring again to Fig. 1(b), a progressive closure of valve A will demonstrate another important feature of hydraulics—the ability to control conveniently the output speed, in a continuous and infinitely variable manner from zero to maximum. As valve A is gradually closed, the pressure of the oil from the pump will rise to maintain the flow of oil delivered through the increasing restriction. At some point this pressure will be sufficient to begin to move the load. Pump flow will then be divided between moving the ram and the "spill" back to tank via valve A.

Since now the load will determine pressure (at a constant value whilst the load rises), the speed of the cylinder will increase gradually as valve A is closed and oil discharge (spill flow) to tank is reduced. In fact, the speed of the cylinder from zero to maximum can be continuously adjusted by opening and closing valve A. As with the ram system described above for Fig. 1(b), a similar situation exists with the motor output shown in Fig. 1(c). In this case, motor speed is controlled by adjusting valve A to control "spill" or by-pass flow. The exact behaviour of speed, pressure and power will depend upon the characteristics of the load, i.e. whether resistance rises or falls with speed. However, the principle of continuously variable speed control is identical. (Figure 3 illustrates the situation graphically where the load is constant.)

1.4.4. Speed/Torque Ratios

With rotary transmissions, limiting the input to output speed and torque ratios are obviously an important feature, particularly in situations which occur in applications such as winch drives. With hydrostatic drives, a simple inherent speed/torque ratio can be conveniently arranged by selecting the relative size of pump and motor.

In Fig. 1(c), with control valve A fully closed and a motor capacity equal to that of the pump, then output speed will equal input speed (neglecting losses), i.e. a speed ratio of 1:1. If a motor of double the capacity per revolution were fitted, the maximum output speed would halve, i.e. a final speed ratio of 2:1. Although not so obvious, to maintain an energy balance the available torque would be doubled for a given power input (see the definitions in Section 6).

In practice, the motor capacity requirement is determined by the maximum torque demanded and the maximum operating pressure selected. The maximum output speed then determines the maximum flow requirement, which in turn dictates the pump capacity for any given prime mover speed. (Of course, fixed ratio input and output gearboxes can also be used to achieve compatible speeds, etc.)

1.4.5. Forward and Reverse

Reverse motion in a cylinder or motor can sometimes be achieved in practice by the equivalent of opening valve A in such circuits as shown in Figs. 1(b) and (c) and allowing the load to reverse the motion by gravity effects.

However, it is usual in circuits other than those involved in raising heavy loads (such as loading doors, etc.) to drive the ram or motor in reverse. Alternative circuits are shown in Fig. 2.

With a cylinder of the double acting type, it is necessary simply to re-route the oil flow into the opposite end of the cylinder, but to reverse a motor involves reversing the direction of flow through the motor. This can be achieved either by using "reversing valves", or in the case of a variable capacity pump it is usually possible to reverse the direction of the delivery flow by moving the control from forward through zero (neutral) into the opposite direction (reverse)—i.e. "overcentre".

1.4.6. Efficiency

Overall efficiency is defined as the following ratio:

$$\frac{\text{Useful or Effective Power Out}}{\text{Total Power Input}}.$$

The overall efficiency of any drive is important since:

a) the total necessary power input should be the minimum to achieve the required output work rate to minimize capital and running costs and reduce prime mover size, etc.

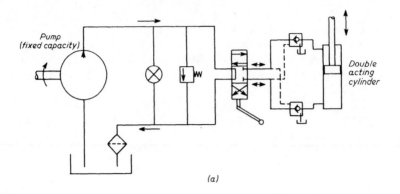

(a)

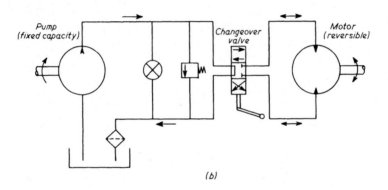

(b)

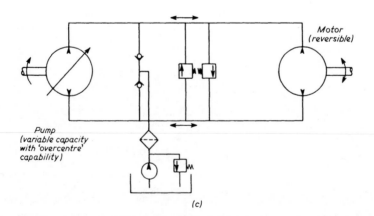

(c)

FIG. 2.—*Three forms of forward/reverse drive circuits.*

b) "wasted" power is lost as heat which may present a problem of overheating.

The inherent efficiency of various circuits, plays an important part in the design of systems and some of the main features are discussed below.

1.4.7. Spill or By-Pass Speed Control

The characteristics of a simple pump/motor system, Fig. 1(c), with spill flow control are presented in Fig. 3. At a partial speed condition, where a large portion of the pump flow is being spilled (i.e. motor speed is low), spill power (spill flow at circuit pressure) is a high proportion of input.

Since no mechanical work is being done with this power and it is converted into heat across the valve A, it can readily be seen that the overall drive efficiency is low and that provision may have to be made to keep the oil cool by fitting an oil–air or oil–water heat exchanger.

Figure 3(e) shows that with valve A closed completely and all oil circulating through the motor, efficiency is a maximum—the only losses being those inherent within the circuit equipment.

In practice, therefore, this type of circuit—which is very commonly used to provide a multitude of both linear and rotary drive requirements—is not acceptable where long periods of part speed running are required or where high powers are involved.

Figure 4(a) shows an alternative description of this situation. Since the pump has been sized to give the maximum flow, when a part speed condition is required the power "lost" in heat is equivalent to the shaded area of the graph.

1.4.8. Double Pumps

One method of improving the situation described above for a single fixed capacity pump circuit is to employ a double pump with an automatic flow control; this combines the deliveries for the maximum flow requirement and selects only one pump output for the higher pressure duties.

This situation is shown in Fig. 4(b) and it can be seen that compared to Fig. 4(a) the shaded area, i.e. the "lost" power, is much reduced. To achieve this system, an unloading valve is required in order to allow the flow from the second pump to by-pass back to the tank at low pressure when the work circuit demands pressure beyond level 1.

1.4.9. Variable Pumps

A complete matching of input and output speed and power can only be achieved by using a variable capacity pump, the various practical alternatives of which are described later in Section 3.

A pump having a fixed delivery per revolution was assumed in the examples described above. However, in practice where part speed is required for long periods, or where higher powers are involved, the power losses associated with spilling flow cannot be tolerated and pumps with a continuously variable capacity are used to achieve output speed changes.

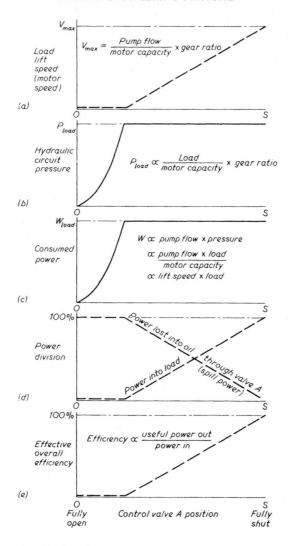

FIG. 3.—*Main characteristics of an open circuit rotary output system driving a winch (constant load).*

Several alternative designs are described later in Section 3, but generally the output control is operated to adjust the pumping volume whilst maintaining pump speed. In this way, only the pump flow required to operate the motor at the desired speed is delivered and the circuit does not require a control valve (A) to by-pass flow (see Fig. 4(c)). In the limit, a "neutral" condition is achieved by having a zero pump capacity.

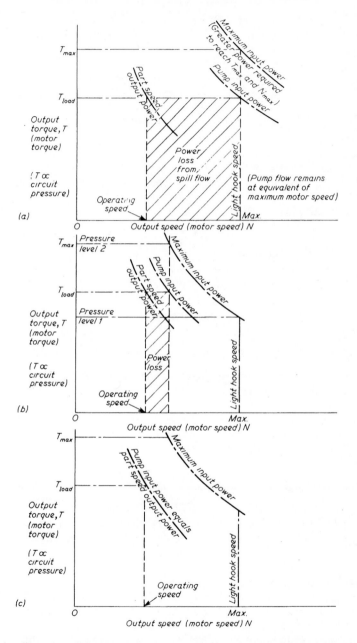

FIG. 4.—*Torque/speed characteristics. (a) Single fixed capacity pump system. (b) Double fixed capacity pump system. (c) Variable fixed capacity pump system.*

This situation is unlike a mechanical neutral condition in that the pump neither delivers nor accepts flow and, hence, the motor cannot overrun or run back—a situation which gives good advantage for "inching", since positive control is maintained at all times.

The reverse drive condition is also simply achieved by a continuous movement of the control lever through the neutral position from "forward" delivery to "reverse".

An important extension of the concept of capacity variation is in the use of automatic or semi-automatic controls to adjust pump output to meet pre-determined criteria, such as a maximum system pressure (output torque) or a maximum input torque to avoid prime mover overload. Some of the various standard controls available are described later in Table I in Section 3.5.

In most instances the variable capacity pump associated with rotary transmissions is of the piston type described in Section 3. In many cases involving a closed circuit, it is necessary to include a small fixed capacity boost pump to pressurize the low pressure side of the main circuit, by means of two low pressure selector valves and a low pressure relief valve, in order to ensure the system is always fully charged with oil. This condition is needed to give a rigid drive at all times and prevent damage to the pump which could occur if it is operated under cavitation conditions for a considerable period.

1.4.10. "Two Speed" and Variable Capacity Motors

Variable capacity motors can provide another method of extending circuit capabilities in a similar way to double or variable pumps. Two general categories can be identified:

a) "Two speed" or switched capacity;
b) Continuously variable capacity between maximum and minimum.

Practical examples of this equipment are described in Section 3 but Fig. 5 illustrates the operational characteristics.

The maximum torque condition can be met with the required capacity at the maximum design pressure as before but the maximum speed can be extended by reducing the motor capacity per revolution. This can be particularly useful to meet "light hook" speeds where low loads are involved.

An alternative viewpoint is the achievement of a similar maximum torque/maximum speed range with a smaller capacity pump.

1.4.11. System Control Valves

Having considered some of the factors governing pump and motor selection in any hydraulic circuit, we shall now turn briefly to the principle features of the control valves.

Undoubtedly, the most important action is provided by the circuit relief valve. This is set to open at the design pressure corresponding to the

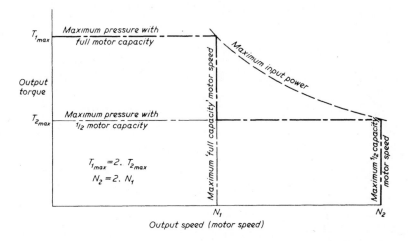

FIG. 5.—*Torque/speed curve for a 2-speed motor* (2:1 *motor capacity variation*).

maximum desired force or torque from the system. When this pressure is achieved, the relief valve opens and spills flow to the tank or low pressure circuit to prevent a further pressure rise. In this way, complete safety is assured both for the circuit components and associated structures, etc. For instance, it is impossible to overload a mooring or winch line and controlled maximum torque can be applied very simply in cargo valve actuation systems.

Simple change-over valves have been mentioned when discussing forward and reverse motor operation, but this type of directional valve plays a very large part in achieving the necessary operations in many applications.

In the majority of designs a simple landed spool geometry is used with various profiles to achieve oil flow direction alteration.

In most cases three positions are available. With manual spool operation, progressive cut-off as well as directional change is available, but a very common range of valves employs solenoid action to push the spool from the centre to either end position.

The convenient control of flow rates, pressure levels and operation sequence is also achieved through the other types of standard valves available to the circuit designer and typical equipment is considered in more detail in Section 3.

2. HYDRAULIC CIRCUIT COMPONENTS— DESIGN PRINCIPLES

Several general design and operating characteristics can be identified for hydraulic power transmission components and these are worth discussing briefly before proceeding to more practical aspects.

Perhaps the most fundamental factor is the self-lubricating nature of almost all mechanisms, which is achieved by use of the working fluid. However, in addition to its use as a lubricant, the working fluid is also used to support high loads through hydrostatic and hydro-dynamic bearings. In this way, particularly in pumps and motors, metal-to-metal loadings are minimized to achieve good reliability, long life and high operating efficiency.

2.1. HYDROSTATIC BEARINGS

Although hydrokinetic and boundary lubrication effects undoubtedly have an influence on the performance of moving parts in any hydraulic circuit component, the generation of load carrying ability through oil velocities or boundary conditions is usually secondary to the effects of the hydrostatic pressure. Discussion will therefore be restricted to an outline of the principles of hydrostatic "balance" employed in the design of many items of hydraulic equipment.

The main characteristics of hydrostatic bearings utilized in hydraulic equipment are demonstrated by considering a round pressure fed pad such as that shown in Fig. 6. The load to be carried is generated by oil pressure P on the piston area A. In order to carry this load most efficiently, assuming it is necessary for the bearing pad to slide, pressure is also fed to the area A' on the pad face. If we examine the pressure across the complete pad face we find pressure levels as shown on the graph, rising across the sealing land from zero to P, with a constant pressure across the pad recess.

Hence, the load carrying ability of the pressurized oil is equal to the combined pressure values over the different areas.

In practice, the diameters d_1 and d_2 are arranged such that the majority of the force PA is taken by the pressure across the pad face leaving, say, 5 per cent load to maintain the piston positively against the bearing face.

The design problem is in fact to achieve a balance between the residual load holding the faces together and the leakage of high pressure oil across the bearing land—this leakage constituting, of course, a power loss in the form of oil heating. In the particular case shown, a restriction may be included in the feed hole between A and A' to increase stability and reduce leakage.

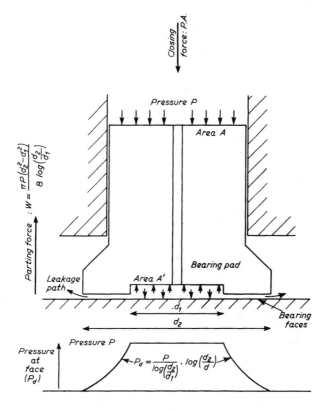

FIG. 6.—*Design principles of a sliding bearing face for a pressure loaded piston.*
(Courtesy Lucas Industrial Equipment Ltd.)

2.2. POSITIVE DISPLACEMENT PUMPS

In order to transmit power, a means must be available to convert mechanical energy in terms of torque and speed into hydraulic pressure and flow. In practice, this conversion is achieved by some form of positive displacement pump.

The many different geometries and designs used in this type of pump are reviewed later in Section 3 but all depend upon the simple principle of trapping a volume of oil in a cavity when the cavity is connected to the inlet port—and then moving this volume to connect with the outlet port, at which point the cavity is discharged.

This pumping action is achieved by causing the cavity to progressively enlarge whilst connected to the inlet, thus drawing in oil and then progressively displacing this oil by reducing the volume, when in connexion with the outlet. In this way, a flow of oil is achieved from inlet to outlet, but at no time is there a direct connexion between the pump ports.

A most important point is that the displaced oil from the cavity must be expelled into the outlet when the pump is operated whatever conditions occur downstream in the hydraulic circuit.

Hence, "positive displacement"—for each revolution of the drive shaft a given quantity of oil is delivered, depending upon the geometry of the mechanism. In many designs the capacity per revolution is a fixed quantity determined by the manufactured size of the pumping components. However, in others the capacity can be varied whilst the pump is operating thus providing the important method of controlling power and speed, referred to earlier.

As already stated, the pump must discharge a given volume of oil per revolution or per time interval (assuming a constant drive speed), but if an unrestricted pipe leads the oil back to the tank and hence eventually returns it to the pump inlet no pressure is generated and no useful work is done. The power absorbed, i.e. required at the pump shaft is only that absorbed in friction within the pump. However, if the pump flow is directed to a cylinder working against a load—such as shown in Fig. 1(b)—then because the pump must deliver fluid, then the load must move. But to move the load the pressure against the piston must create the necessary force, equal to the load plus friction.

Hence, pressure rises due to the presence of the load or resistance, until that load is overcome and the piston moves at a speed which is governed by the pump flow rate and the piston area. The pressure, which is transmitted equally to all parts of the fluid, reacts against the walls of the pumping cavities and this results in a reaction turning moment at the pump shaft. Hence, force at the pump shaft—in the form of a driving torque—is transmitted to the piston and load. The mechanical advantage of such an arrangement depends upon the ratio of pump capacity per revolution and the area of the piston.

It is hoped that the above description will dispel a common misconception. Pumps do not pump pressure, they pump only oil; it is the load or restriction which causes the pump to generate pressure in the circuit. If the load is such that increasing force is required to move that load at increasing speed, then as pump speed or capacity is increased to increase delivered flow, pressure will also rise—but only as a result of the load characteristic. Similarly, if pump flow is restricted by closing a valve, pressure will rise as the pump maintains its discharge through the restriction.

This basic principle holds true whatever the type of positive displacement pump and circuit.

In engineering reality, the mechanical design of the pumping mechanism sets a practical limit to the pressure that any particular pump can produce.

Typical limitations are indicated in the description of practical examples later. As is to be expected, costs and performance in pressure/power/speed/ efficiency, are largely interchangeable and the technical/commercial decision can be complex in any given circumstance.

3. PRACTICAL HYDRAULIC EQUIPMENT

3.1. GEAR PUMPS

Several relatively simple mechanisms utilize the action of meshed teeth to achieve delivery of fluid without reciprocating parts or valves. The main alternative geometries are considered in turn and it will be clear that each offers some particular advantage.

3.1.1. The External Gear Pump

This design is the most commonly used in all areas of engineering. The basic geometry is shown in Fig. 7. As the driven gear is rotated, the volume between the teeth in region A expands thus drawing in fluid. This fluid is then trapped and drawn round in the peripheral cavities of the driven and idler gears. As these cavities cross the outlet port, the cavity volume decreases as the teeth mesh (region B) and this ejects the oil into the outlet port. Since almost no oil volume exists at section C, the expelled volume is approximately equivalent to the cavity volume. The pumped volume or capacity per revolution is, therefore, proportional to gear pitch, radius and width.

Since this is a positive displacement device, any restriction (i.e. "load") on the outlet will result in pressure being developed in the oil to overcome the resistance and hence the sealing areas formed by the teeth flanks, tips and faces (region C) must be adequate. The tip clearance in the body cavity and tooth face mating obviously depend directly upon machining tolerances and surface finishes. The same could be said of the gear flanks since gear width is equally important, but in this area a major improvement in overall performance is achieved by introducing compensation plates which form the side walls against the gear faces.

These plates are pressure balanced to be loaded against the gears, and the leakage paths between plate and body are closed off by rubber seals. In this way, not only can initial machining tolerances be relaxed but body distortions due to pressure loading are compensated by the elasticity in the seal, and leakage is considerably reduced.

Two examples of gear pumps are illustrated in Figs 8 and 9 but a similar construction is used in the majority of comparable equipment currently available. Both plain and roller bearings are used, the former usually being restricted to smaller sizes.

An important aspect in the design of the gear pump is the inherently high out-of-balance loading caused by the high pressure fluid on one side only of the gears. This feature and the problems of achieving adequate sealing at the gear tips and sides restricts the maximum practical pressures obtainable with this type of pump.

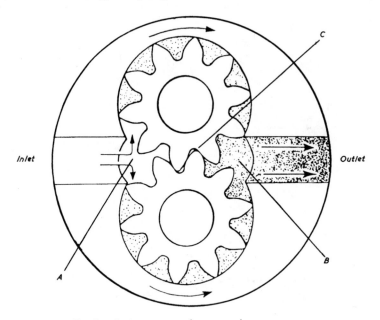

Fig. 7.—*Basic geometry of an external gear pump.*

The normal pressure rating is 140–175 bar (2–2500 lbf/in^2) although designs are now available which operate up to 210 bar (3000 lbf/in^2), and higher for short periods. Speed ranges vary from a maximum of 2000 rev/min for larger sizes, up to 6000 rev/min for the smallest sizes. The method of construction which is usually employed enables a large size range to be offered by simply varying the gear face widths. For increased output or supplies to two or more separate circuits, in-line tandem combinations can be obtained. A typical arrangement is shown in Fig. 9.

The basic design is also available for use as a motor, the only differences between pump and motor being in the detailed internal pressure balancing/sealing arrangements.

Compared to other designs, the external gear motor has a poor starting characteristic and both pumps and motors tend to have a lower overall efficiency. However, continuous improvements are still being achieved through programmes of design and development carried out by the main manufacturers.

FIG. 8.—*Hydraulic gear pump and motor.*

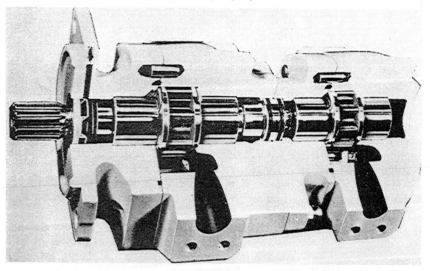

FIG. 9.—*Sectioned view of an external gear pump—double unit—showing gear side plates.*
(Courtesy Hamworthy Engineering Ltd.)

3.1.2. The Internal Gear Pump

This term is used loosely to cover several alternative geometries of the external design described above. The driven gear has externally cut teeth, which mesh with internally cut teeth in the idler.

Geometric differences exist in the tooth profile and methods of sealing used to achieve a sealed volume and give a positive displacement of fluid from inlet to outlet.

Figure 10 shows one common arrangement known as the "Gerotor". Here, the inner driven element has one less tooth than the outer and a series of pockets is formed which progressively expand and contract as the gears rotate. By arranging kidney ports (shown dotted) in the body of the unit, fluid is drawn in through the inlet and expelled into the outlet. From the two illustrations, it can be seen that as the rolling action proceeds between inner and outer gears, the sealing position between incoming and outgoing fluid moves progressively around the entire profile.

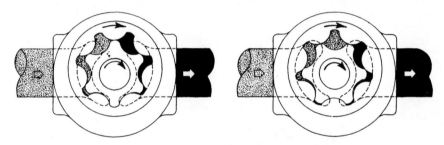

FIG. 10.—*Geometry of a "Gerotor" type pumping element.*

Design and manufacturing factors are similar to the "external" pump, although a tight tolerance chamber width is generally relied upon to seal gear faces and "compensating" plates are not employed.

An operating advantage is claimed because the relative speed of the two gear elements is low at the meshing interfaces and the plain outer bearing of the idler can very adequately carry the imposed loads.

An alternative geometry is shown in Fig. 11. In this design internal and external teeth tips form the seal against a crescent shaped metal segment which is part of the body.

The pumping action is, in many ways, similar to the external gear type of pump. The expansion of the intertooth volume at region A draws in oil, and the divided chamber is then carried round inside and outside the inner segment. In region B, the teeth begin to mesh and so reduce the intertooth cavity, hence expelling oil into the outlet port. An example of this type of pump is shown in Fig. 12. In this particular range, two or three gear pairs are mounted into a common body and driven from the same shaft. Fluid is pumped from the first stage into the second and then to the third before reaching the outlet. Pressure is raised progressively at each stage.

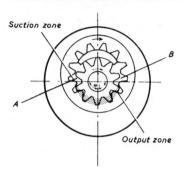

Fig. 11.—*Alternative geometry of internal gear with sealing crescent.*

With a restricted single stage pressure rise, life, reliability and efficiency are improved. Maximum continuous pressure for this design is 310 bar (4500 lbf/in^2).

The type of pump shown in Fig. 12 also has a very low noise level, which is an important advantage in certain applications.

Fig. 12.—*Multi-stage gear pump with exceptionally low noise levels (using the geometry of Fig. 11).*

(Courtesy Keelavite Hydraulics Ltd.)

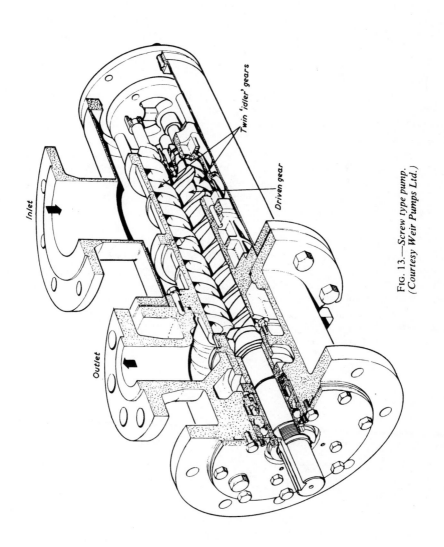

FIG. 13.—Screw type pump.
(Courtesy Weir Pumps Ltd.)

3.2. Screw Pumps

In this design, the "gear" teeth are extended helically along the axis to form a scroll. A similar scroll on the idler meshes to form cavities to carry the oil axially along the length of the "gear" from inlet to outlet.

This is illustrated in Fig. 13. In this case, two idlers are incorporated and since pressures are symmetrical about the central driven member, side loads on the drive shaft are reduced.

3.3. Vane Pumps and Motors

In many applications the fixed capacity vane pump is employed in place of the gear pump. In its simplest form this type of equipment employs a set of vanes which are held in a rotor running eccentrically inside a circular chamber to provide continuously expanding and contracting volumes; thus moving oil between the inlet and outlet side ports. As with gear pumps, high out-of-balance forces are an inherent feature of this simple geometry and to eliminate these forces on the bearings, the main chamber is made elliptical to allow a double pumping action through two pairs of ports diametrically opposed. A typical geometry is shown in Fig. 14, and a practical example is shown in Fig. 15.

Centrifugal force on the vanes keeps them in contact with the outer track to maintain a seal, but in some designs springs and pressure fed areas beneath the vanes are also used to maintain volumetric efficiency at higher pressures without excessive wear. Vane tip and track conditions are the main limitations on the performance rating of this type of pump.

The usual maximum working pressure for vane pumps is 140–175 bar (2–2500 lbf/in^2) with speeds up to 2000 rev/min. Like gear units, tandem combinations are available as standard.

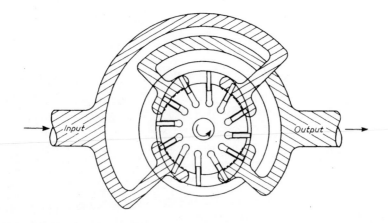

Fig. 14.—*Geometry of balanced vane pump.*

FIG. 15.—*Vane pump.*
(Courtesy Sperry-Vickers Ltd.)

Vane units are generally of the fixed capacity type but variable capacity types with automatic control to constant pressure are widely used in certain applications to provide a constant pressure power source. Here, a single eccentric cam is used and the pressure forces are balanced against a spring and piston connected to the delivery port.

Depending upon the spring setting, when a certain delivery pressure is reached the eccentricity of the outer ring is progressively reduced, thus reducing output flow. This type of pump normally operates to 140 bar (2000 lbf/in^2) at 1500 rev/min.

3.4. CAM ROTOR TYPE PUMPS

This particular type of fixed capacity pump and motor is a further alternative to gear or vane units. In this design the positive displacement of oil is achieved through rotating an elliptically shaped rotor within a circular chamber, with twin vanes, or "brushes" to divide inlet from outlet and produced a balanced pressure distribution (see Figs 16(a) and (b)).

The normal maximum pressure for such equipment is 140 bar (2000 lbf/in^2) (210 bar (3000 lbf/in^2) intermittent) with speeds up to 3000 rev/min. Tandem combinations are available.

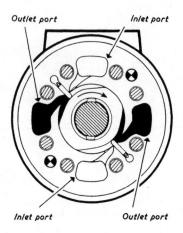

FIG. 16(a).—*Section through cam-rotor type pump.*

FIG. 16(b).—*Typical cam-rotor type pump.*

3.5. AXIAL PISTON PUMPS AND MOTORS

A number of basic types of piston equipment are available. In all cases, the pumping action is achieved with reciprocating pistons and in the majority of designs variable output flow capacity is readily obtained—the method depending upon the detailed geometry of the machine. The simplest design is usually described as the swashplate type and the concept is illustrated in Fig. 17. A practical example is shown in Fig. 18.

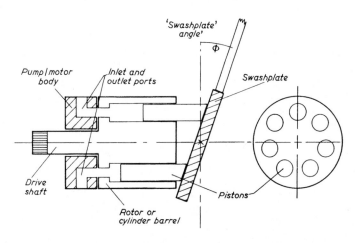

FIG. 17.—*Basic geometry of axial piston pump/motor.*

Multiple pistons are positioned axially in a rotor, which is connected to the prime mover via the drive shaft. As the rotor revolves, the cylinders follow the path of the kidney-shaped inlet port. The angle of the swashplate causes the pistons to move in the cylinder bores away from the kidney port, thus allowing fluid to enter the cylinder. Further movement brings the cylinder on to the path of the outlet kidney port and causes the piston to move downwards; this expels fluid through the outlet port. Both the rotor face and the "slipper pads" on the piston ends are pressure balanced and lubricated to minimize power losses. With variable capacity units the angle of the swashplate is altered and the output flow varied proportionally. If the swashplate is moved "over centre", the direction of the flow is reversed.

The forces involved with small pumps allow the volume to be varied mechanically, but on the larger sizes the forces increase to such a magnitude that some form of servo assistance is essential. This takes the form of an internal piston operated through a simple servo arrangement and which takes its power from the high pressure pump output (see Figs 18 and 19).

The basic simplicity of this type of equipment allows a compact variable capacity unit to be produced capable of operating as pump or motor in either direction of rotation. The control can be readily adapted for operation by means of hand wheels or levers, or for remote actuation by electrical, hydraulic or pneumatic signals. Also, a range of automatic or semi-automatic controls can be incorporated to simplify the operators task and improve safety whilst increasing work rates. A summary of the control types available for one particular range of pumps is given in Table I.

A second form of swashplate pump employs a stationary block carrying the pistons which are oscillated through a rotating swashplate mechanism. Input and output flow passes through non-return valves connected to the individual cylinders.

The third form is particularly well established in Continental Europe. In this design the rotating cylinder barrel or rotor is tilted (together with the porting faces) at an angle to the input drive shaft to produce the basic piston oscillation.

This design produces particularly compact fixed capacity units but leads to greater bulk with variable capacity types, since the complete rotor bearing assembly has to be swung about the drive axis (see Fig. 20).

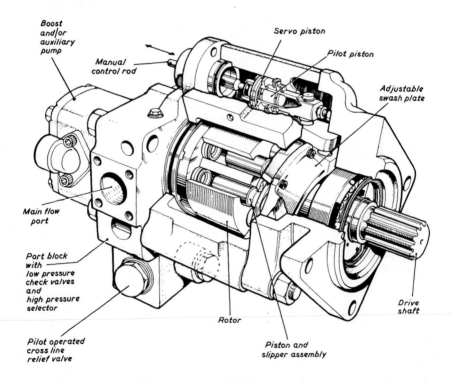

FIG. 18.—*Variable capacity axial piston swashplate pump with integral valves and through shaft driving boost and auxiliary pumps.*
(Courtesy Lucas Industrial Equipment Ltd.)

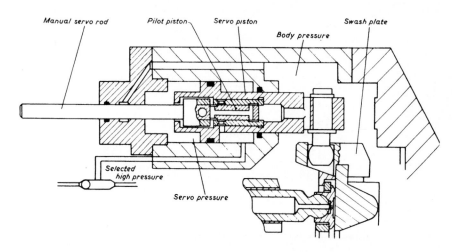

Manual servo rod Pilot piston Servo piston Swash plate
Body pressure
Selected high pressure
Servo pressure

FIG. 19.—*Servo-assisted manual control of swashplate angle.*
(Courtesy Lucas Industrial Equipment Ltd.)

Several variations of this geometry are in use. In some designs the "rotor barrel" is driven round by a universal joint from the drive head, whereas in others the rotor is allowed to lag and is driven by the "connecting" rods through the cylinder walls.

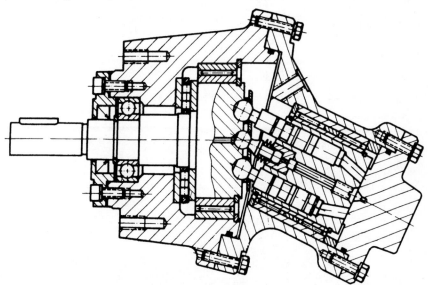

FIG. 20.—*"Bent axis" piston pump geometry*
(Courtesy Hydraulics and Pneumatics Ltd.)

TABLE I—A SUMMARY OF TYPICAL PISTON PUMP AND MOTOR CONTROL TYPES

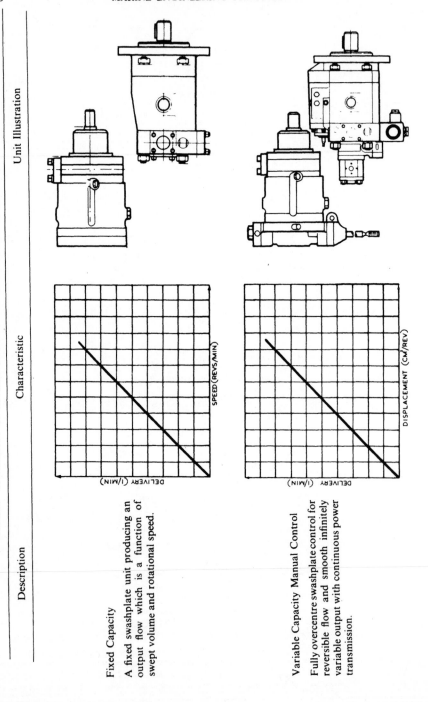

Description	Characteristic	Unit Illustration

Fixed Capacity

A fixed swashplate unit producing an output flow which is a function of swept volume and rotational speed.

Variable Capacity Manual Control

Fully overcentre swashplate control for reversible flow and smooth infinitely variable output with continuous power transmission.

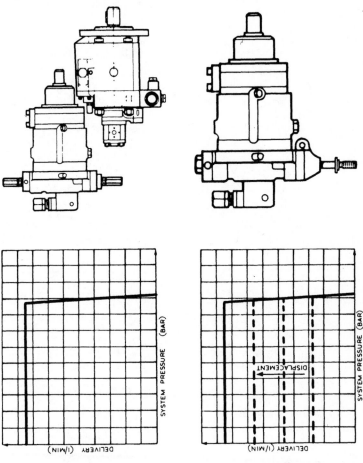

Automatic Pressure Compensation

Variable swashplate pump with automatic stroke control to provide a constant pressure at the pump outlet. Maximum and minimum stroke stops are provided. Pressure valve vent allows independent pressure control or complete off-load. Minimizes power wastage, reduces oil heating and improves system response.

Manual Control with Pressure Override

Provides manual variable control (but not overcentre), with automatic maximum pressure override.

TABLE I—continued.

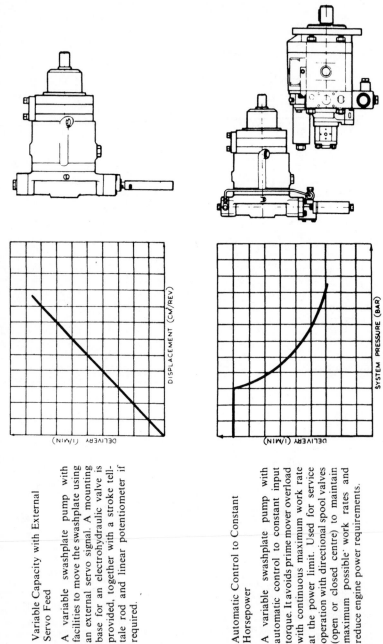

Variable Capacity with External Servo Feed

A variable swashplate pump with facilities to move the swashplate using an external servo signal. A mounting base for an electrohydraulic valve is provided, together with a stroke tell-tale rod and linear potentiometer if required.

Automatic Control to Constant Horsepower

A variable swashplate pump with automatic control to constant input torque. It avoids prime mover overload with continuous maximum work rate at the power limit. Used for service operation with directional spool valves (open or closed centre) to maintain maximum possible work rates and reduce engine power requirements.

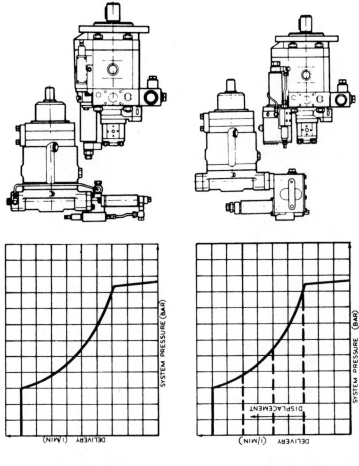

Constant Horsepower with Pressure Override

When maximum pressure condition is reached at the power setting pump swashplate reduces towards zero output. Reduces power wastage and heat generation.

Manual Variable with Automatic Horsepower Control

(With or without pressure override). Combines simple manual operation with anti-stall override to limit input torque demand of the system. Automatically avoids prime mover overload—reducing operator skill and fatigue for full output working.

TABLE 1—*continued.*

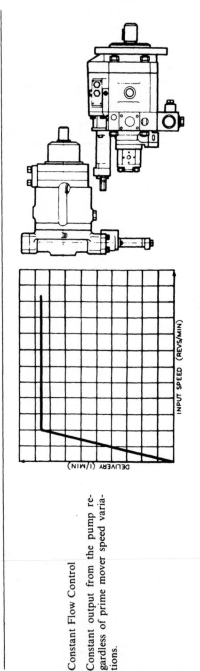

Constant Flow Control

Constant output from the pump regardless of prime mover speed variations.

Other control variations include:

(a) Remote Control: Hydraulic remote control of pump or motor stroke in response to a variable pressure signal. Alternatively electric motor stroke actuation can be supplied.

(b) Neutral Seeking: A simple spring arrangement to positively return the pump to neutral stroke and also to provide a "neutral feel" to the operator.

(c) Variable Sensitivity Linkage: A two-input linkage providing hand and foot control of the transmission, with variable sensitivity to give precise control for manoeuvring.

(d) Coupled Constant Power Controls: Enables two pumps to be operated with power sharing, by using a control signal developed from the separate systems.

(e) Cable Controls: Provide a single remote lever to operate either pump, or both pump and motor sequentially if variable motors are used.

A further axial piston design found in the marine field is illustrated in Fig. 21. In this case the pistons are fixed to the tilting head, which rotates together with the rotor barrel carrying the pistons.

In all rotating barrel types the porting arrangements for entry and exit of the fluid are similar, with crescent or kidney-shaped porting, connected to inlet and outlet.

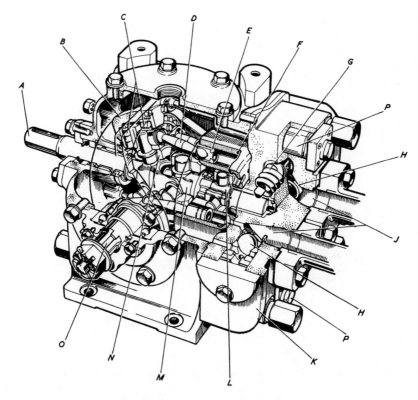

A. *Input shaft*
B. *Tilting box*
C. *Roller bearings*
D. *Connecting rod*
E. *Piston*
F. *Cylinder barrel*

G. *Relief valve*
H. *Replenishing valve*
J. *Ports*
K. *Valve plate*
L. *Barrel joint*
M. *Universal joint*
N. *Socket ring*
O. *Control trunnion*
P. *Control cylinder*

FIG. 21.—*"Tilting head" axial piston pump.*
(Courtesy Vickers Ltd.)

Detailed design variations occur in areas such as the rotating porting face of the rotor barrel to achieve a satisfactory bearing and sealing face. Other critical areas include the method of drive connexion to the rotor and the design of the "slipper pad" on the piston ends.

Generally, equipment is capable of working to maximum pressures of 350 bar (5000 lbf/in^2) with speeds up to 3000 rev/min. Maximum power capability of the largest units is of the order of 224 kW.

3.6. IN-LINE PISTON PUMPS

As their name suggests, in-line pumps have their cylinders arranged in line and the drive is achieved through either eccentric cams or cranks and connecting rods.

Piston rod and crank designs include both larger designs where piston rod and crank are separated from the working fluid by suitable glands, as well as designs where the mechanism is immersed in working fluid (Fig. 22). The former types of pump are particularly suitable for pumping water and other low lubricity fluids, but at the penalty of considerable increase in bulk.

The operating speeds of the connecting rod type of pump are generally lower than other designs, but high flow output can be achieved.

FIG. 22.—*Self-lubricating in-line piston pump with connecting rod and crank mechanism.*

Other equipment using eccentric cams for piston drive is usually of smaller capacity, but direct drive from an electric motor at 1440 rev/min is possible. With this type of pump pressures exceeding 690 bar (10 000 lbf/in^2) are regularly achieved.

3.7. RADIAL PISTON PUMPS

This type of pump is usually fixed capacity per revolution, with a single eccentric but in some designs the eccentricity can be adjusted to vary output.

Figure 23 shows a particular design with a ball and poppet valve arrangement used to achieve an effective pumping action. This type of pump generally gives lower flows than other designs, but the simple geometry is capable of achieving high pressures, e.g. up to 414 bar (6000 lbf/in^2).

3.8. MOTORS

Most designs of positive displacement mechanism are capable of acting as pump or motor. The principles of pumping have been described above but if instead of driving the shaft, fluid is introduced into the inlet port at some pressure then in many designs the mechanism will rotate and in turn drive the shaft. The efficiency achieved for this action depends upon the mechanical arrangement.

Several particular unit designs are widely employed however where this "reversal" is not possible and these are described later.

External Gear, Vane and Axial Piston geometries are generally reversible, with detailed design differences between pumps and motors to achieve optimum performance in each case.

Speeds achieved are comparable with pumps but without the practical restrictions imposed by a prime mover, speeds up to 4000 or 6000 rev/min are possible with smaller sizes. Output torques vary between 21 Nm (15 lbf ft) and 1360 Nm (1000 lbf ft) for a typical range of piston motors.

Obviously, the relatively low output torque from the majority of pump/motor equipment results in the requirement for some form of speed reduction gearbox in many cases to achieve acceptable torque levels for winch drives for instance. This arrangement can be entirely satisfactory but an alternative approach is also possible using equipment of inherently lower speed and higher output torque capability.

3.9. SLOW SPEED HIGH TORQUE MOTORS

A number of different designs of "slow speed" motors are available and are commonly used in marine systems such as winch drives. Most are generally of much higher capacity per revolution than the pump/motor types described above.

Three design alternatives are illustrated here. The first (Figs 24(a) and (b)) shows a typical radial piston unit, with pistons and connecting rods, operated via a single throw eccentric.

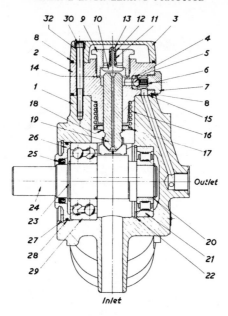

Outlet

Inlet

SECTION AA

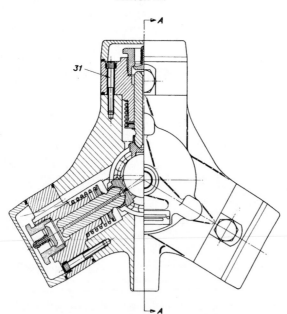

FIG. 23.—*Radial piston pump.*
(Courtesy Andrew Fraser Ltd.)

1. Body (pump)	17. Plate
2. Body (cylinder)	18. Circlip
3. Cover (cylinder)	19. Piston assembly
4. Seat (outlet)	20. Circlip
5. Ball	21. Bearing (end)
6. Spring	22. Circlip
7. Body (outlet)	23. Circlip
8. O-ring	24. Shaft
9. Body (inlet)	25. Seal (shaft)
10. Valve (inlet)	26. Housing
11. Spring	27. Circlip
12. Collar	28. O-ring
13. Nut	29. Bearing (side)
14. Washer	30. Screw
15. O-ring	31. Screw
16. Spring	32. Washer

Key to FIG. 23 (opposite)

FIG. 24(a).—Five piston radial slow speed high torque motor.

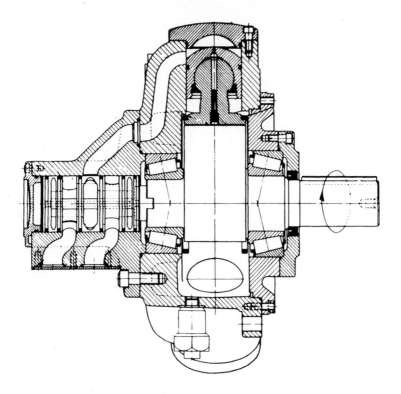

FIG. 24(b).—*Five piston radial slow speed high torque motor—internal arrangement.*
(Courtesy Chamberlain Industries Ltd.)

Flow of fluid to and from pistons is through the central pintle. In the latest designs of this motor, cam eccentricity can be varied through an independent hydraulic supply, giving smoothly varying capacity.

An example of an alternative design is shown in Fig. 25. This is similarly radial in operation but here the pistons operate "inwardly", the oscillating movement being obtained from an internal "multi-lobed" cam profile around the periphery. In this typical example, eight pistons run against a six-lobe track. Therefore, each of the eight pistons makes six oscillations in each revolution. One feature of this type of motor is that the number of working pistons can be reduced by suitable internal porting, thus obtaining the "step change" in capacity referred to earlier. Typically, ranges of this type of motor are capable of developing between 500 Nm (350 lbf ft) to 40 000 Nm (30 000 lbf ft) with maximum speeds of 500 and 100 rev/min, respectively. With certain equipment, torques of 130 000 Nm (95 000 lbf ft) are available directly with a maximum speed of 16 rev/min.

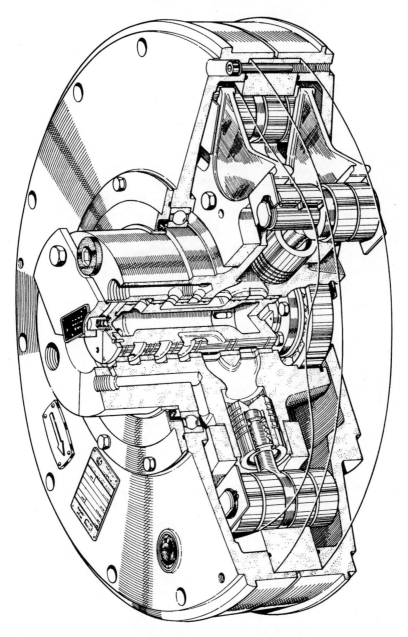

FIG. 25.—*Radial piston multi-lobe slow speed high torque motor.*
(Courtesy Hägglund and Söner AB.)

FIG. 26(a).—*Compact motor using internal gear principle.*

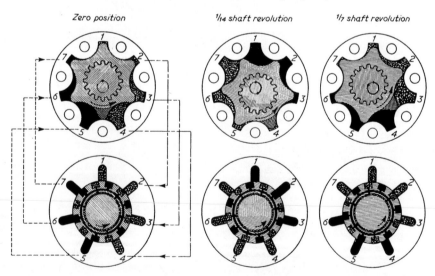

FIG. 26(b).—*Basic geometry of porting arrangement and gear elements.*
(Courtesy Adan Ltd.)

A useful design manufactured in a range of sizes is based on the "Gerotor" type of element shown in Fig. 10. In this motor design, a rotary flow divider valve is used to feed the oil to the fluid chambers in such a way that an inbuilt speed reduction and torque multiplication is achieved in a very compact manner. An example of this type of fixed capacity motor is shown in Figs 26(a) and (b). Maximum speeds for this type of motor range from some 250 rev/min for units developing 1400 Nm (1000 lbf ft) at 100 bar (1400 lbf/in^2) maximum pressure, to 750 rev/min for units giving 140 Nm (100 lbf ft) at 125 bar (1800 lbf/in^2) maximum pressure.

3.10. CYLINDERS

Cylinders, or rams, are the commonest form of drive in a hydraulic system. They provide linear mechanical power in the form of stroke and thrust.

Whereas many types of pumps and motors exist which are based on entirely different geometries, cylinders have a common geometry basically similar to that shown in Fig. 27. However, differences in construction

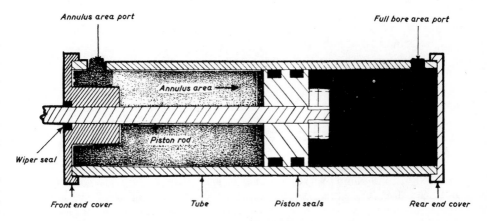

FIG. 27.—*Basic cylinder arrangement.*

methods exist and a range of different mounting methods are supplied to suit the wide variety of installation requirements. In addition, features such as cushioning are essential in certain circuits. The main points of construction are summarised below.

3.10.1. Cylinder Barrel

(a) *Tie Bars*—convenient for manufacturing—bulk and tie rod stretch make unsuitable for heavier duties.

(b) *Screwed End Covers*—cheap to produce especially in large quantities. Neat External appearance.

(c) *Tapped Barrel*—suitable for thick walled, heavy duty cylinders—robust and compact.

(d) *Welded End Caps*—most suitable for small disposable cylinders.

The method used can depend upon the application requirements, such as ease of servicing, minimum first cost, or minimum dimensions.

3.10.2. Cylinder Stresses

The design criteria required to make a cylinder suitable for a particular situation are well established. Formulae for determining the wall thickness to resist the hoop stress produced by a given hydraulic pressure are readily available and many cylinders are produced from cold drawn and honed steel tube supplied in standard bore and wall thicknesses.

3.10.3. Piston and Piston Rod

The piston rod must not only transmit the cylinder force, it must also extend against the gland and wiper seals without damage.

Case hardening is usually employed to give the rod a tough surface resistant to damage; and bright chrome, hard chrome and nickel finishes give corrosion protection. Alternatively, for marine installations, stainless steel rods may be employed.

A variety of methods of attaching the piston to the rod include screwing and locking, and screw and nut.

3.10.4. Piston Rods

Another important factor is the diameter of the piston rod which must be considered, when extended, as a strut subjected to tensile or buckling forces.

Side loading of the piston rod should, of course, be eliminated or reduced to a minimum by selecting the best possible mounting arrangement, but deflection due to the weight of the cylinder and rod must be taken into account when an unsupported horizontal mounting is required.

These considerations are particularly important on cylinders with eye mountings on the rod and head ends as these provide the only support.

Essentially, therefore, the piston rod diameter is determined by load, stroke and mounting style.

For long applications, a stop tube or spacer may be fitted on the rod between the gland and piston to provide an additional bearing support.

3.10.5. Mountings

Typical standard mounting variations are shown in Fig. 28 for a tie rod construction.

3.10.6. Seals

In most cases, four sealing requirements must be met:
1) Static barrel seals;
2) Piston seals;
3) Gland seals;
4) Wiper seals.

O-rings can be used universally for the static seals, but the dynamic requirements are more complex.

Piston seals are basically concerned with reducing leakage and friction irrespective of the pressure. A piston without seals will function but the leakage rate past the piston is usually unacceptable in terms of power loss. This loss can be reduced to a low level, or virtually eliminated, according to the type of sealing selected and the operating characteristics required.

Many medium and high pressure cylinders use multiple automotive type cast iron piston rings which give a long operating life, especially at elevated pressures. However, some leakage will occur with this type of piston seal assembly and whilst this may not be critical in most cases, it is clearly not acceptable for applications where a very fine feed rate is demanded or where the piston must be held in a particular stroke position.

3.10.7. Elastomer Seals

Specially formulated elastomer seals are widely used, particularly in cylinders intended for general purpose applications. These are specialized products developed by the seal manufacturers and quite often a seal is designed to suit a particular area of application. Piston head seal assemblies with V-ring, T-ring and U-ring configurations are used but always the problem is to ensure efficient sealing, long-life, low friction and good performance at both low and high pressures. Obviously, the quality of the bore finish is a factor and this becomes even more critical if very low "break away" forces are required. Seals made from P.T.F.E. (Teflon, Fluon, Viton) are often preferred for cylinders where very low friction and "stick slip" characteristics are required. The type of hydraulic fluid is also important. If a conventional light, low viscosity, hydraulic oil is being used, then this will have good lubricating properties; but if the application demands one of the fire resistant fluids, then a different seal material is necessary.

Seals made from fluoro–carbon elastomers are favoured for fluids of the phosphate ester type or where cylinders must be operated at elevated temperature.

A gland seal is necessary to prevent leakage of oil along the piston rod, while a wiper seal will give a wiping action on the rod to provide a lubricating film and at the same time prevent dirt entering the gland. V-rings are popular for piston rod sealing but U-rings and other variations are also used. Synthetic gland and wiper seals are common although leather has useful

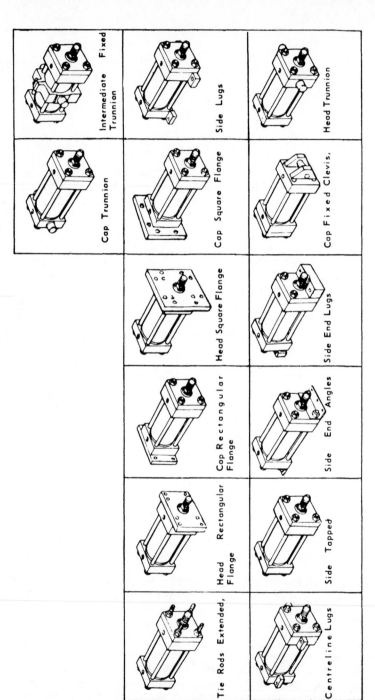

FIG. 28.—*Alternative cylinder mountings.*

characteristics, such as low friction, when used with water emulsions. Metal wiper seals are often recommended for applications where the rod is likely to be in contact with gummy substances.

When considering gland seals, an important aspect is maintenance and accessibility for changing a seal with the minimum of down time. Some designs have a cartridge assembly which incorporates the gland and wiper seals so that they may be replaced as one unit.

3.10.8. Cushioning

With high piston speeds, or if the piston rod is connected to a heavy load, then it is desirable to decelerate the piston towards the end of its stroke—this provides a smoother action on the load itself, puts less strain on the cylinder reduces hydraulic shock and helps to keep down the noise level. The method of achieving a cushioning effect varies according to the degree of control required, but the principle is to interrupt the flow of oil leaving the cylinder at a point near the end of the stroke and direct it through an orifice. During what remains of the stroke, the momentum of the piston rod assembly and the load is dissipated by the energy loss of the fluid passing through the orifice at high velocity.

A typical arrangement is shown in Fig. 29 where, towards the end of the stroke, a small volume of oil is trapped and must pass through a needle valve orifice A, which is usually adjustable so that the rate of deceleration can be controlled. A non-return valve, B, is incorporated so that when the piston is required to move in the opposite direction system pressure can be applied on both the annulus area and the end of the cushion plunger.

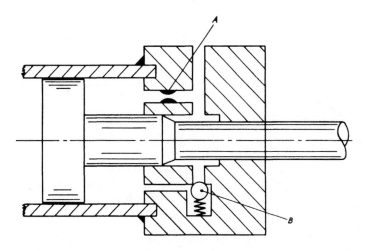

FIG. 29.—*Typical cylinder cushioning arrangement.*

With built-in cushioning methods it is necessary to ensure that excessively high fluid pressures do not occur. If the resulting pressures would be too high, then external valves must be used to provide the required deceleration rate. One method is to use a normally open spring-loaded, two-port valve which can be closed by the piston rod engaging a cam at the appropriate point in the stroke. This causes the oil to be exhausted through a relief valve and adjustable needle valve, allowing the rate of deceleration to be smoothly controlled. A solenoid operated valve may be used as an alternative to the mechanical valve.

3.10.9. Circuit Design—Single and Double Acting Cylinders

The single acting cylinder is the simplest form where pressure is applied to the full area of the piston head to move the load through piston rod extension. The load causes rod retraction when the drive pressure is released.

The most common form of hydraulic cylinder is the double acting type shown in Fig. 27 with a single piston rod passing through one end cover. This type of cylinder is applied so that the maximum load is moved when the pressure is acting on the full area of the piston and not on the retraction stroke.

In some cases, it may be necessary to have an equal force applied in either direction of stroke and also to have the same speed of stroking. This can be obtained by having a through-rod cylinder or by using a standard cylinder in which the rod area is equal to half the piston area. Valving is then arranged so that pressure is applied either to the annulus area alone or to both the annulus and piston areas simultaneously. If flow at a fixed rate is then fed to the annulus area, the piston will retract at a constant speed, while if the same flow is fed to both the annulus and the piston areas, the rod will extend at the same speed in the opposite direction since the fluid displaced from the annulus area augments the constant input flow (see Fig. 30).

3.11. Semi-Rotary Actuators

Figure 31 is a schematic diagram of a double vane type of rotary or torque actuator, a simple device for producing reciprocating rotary power.

Torque actuators consist of a cylindrical chamber containing a stationary barrier or shoe and a central shaft on which one (or two) vanes are fixed. The assembly is enclosed by end caps through which the shaft projects. By applying oil pressure to the vane or vanes rotary motion is achieved. Motion is limited in the single vane unit to approximately 280°. The use of two vanes doubles the torque level but restricts movement to some 100°.

This type of equipment can offer advantages over cylinders and torque arms where relatively high turning movements are required but space is limited.

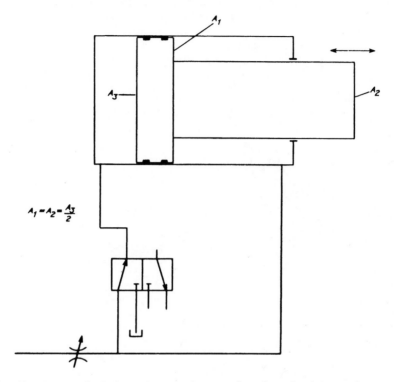

FIG. 30.—*Circuit and cylinder to obtain equal power and speed in either direction of movement.*

3.12. BASIC CIRCUIT CONTROL VALVES

As indicated earlier, any hydraulic circuit includes a variety of valves to regulate pressure or flow conditions to control force, torque, speed and/or the direction of movement of the system output. The large range of alternative proprietary equipment available can be considered for convenience in three separate groups:

Flow control;
Pressure control;
Directional control.

The following text and illustrations, together with Table II, cover the majority of the standard equipment used in any hydraulic system. In practice, all valves are available in alternative forms for mounting either directly into pipelines or on machined manifold blocks and baseplates. In the latter cases, international standards are now widely recognized for the dimensional layout of porting and fixing interfaces.

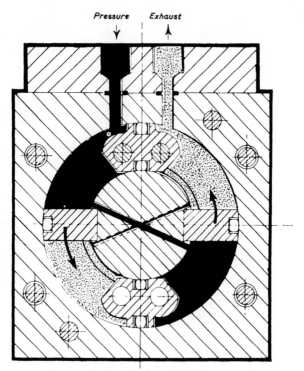

Fig. 31.—*Double vane semi-rotary actuator.*

3.12.1. Non-return or Check Valves

These are the simplest form of valve (Fig. 32) and play a very important part in hydraulic systems by preventing interaction between different parts of the circuit. They may be of in-line or gasket-mounted type, according to the requirements of the installation, and usually consist of a ball or poppet held on to a seat by means of a low force spring. While the unit may be capable of withstanding high pressures, the pressure drop across the units—as determined by the spring—is usually low.

The pressure of the oil stream entering the inlet port causes the poppet to lift from its seat and allow oil to pass to the outlet port. If there is any tendency for flow to reverse, i.e. if oil tends to enter the outlet port, then this action reinforces the spring, returning the ball or poppet to its seat. Any further increase in this return pressure merely seats the poppet more firmly.

3.12.2. Pilot Operated Non-Return or Check Valves

If it is required to allow oil to return through the check valve, arrangements are made to lift the poppet from its seat by the application of pilot pressure. In this case, pressure is applied to a suitably sized piston to push the poppet off its seat by means of a push rod.

Direction of free flow

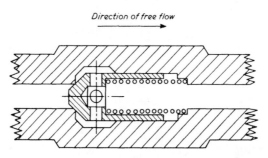

Fig. 32.—*In-line non-return valve.*

3.12.3. Pressure Control Valves

There are two main types of pressure control valve—relief and reducing, the basic difference being that the relief valve is *closed* by a spring, and the reducing valve *opened* by a spring.

(a) *Relief Valves*

These are used to protect the system from over pressure and are of two main types—direct acting Fig. 33 and pilot operated (or balanced piston) Fig. 34.

The direct acting relief valve is used for controlling low flows and may be used for pressures up to 172 bar (2500 lbf/in^2) or higher.

For higher pressures and larger flows, pilot operated valves are used. This type of valve, in conjunction with a variable orifice and suitable circuitry, can also be used for bleed off control (see 3.12.4 below).

In the pilot operated type of relief valve in Fig. 34(a), the main piston is retained in the closed position by a light spring. The pressure on either side of the piston is balanced through a jet. Pressurized oil enters port A and pressure is applied to both ends of the piston.

When the pressure on the pilot valve exceeds the setting of the spring the ball lifts, allowing a flow to take place through the jet causing a pressure drop.

This causes a pressure differential between the top and bottom of the piston and the main pressure then overcomes the piston spring pushing the piston down. Oil can now flow from A to B.

When control pressure falls below the setting of the pilot valve, flow ceases to take place through the jet and pressure on each end of the piston is equalized. The spring then closes the piston, cutting off the connexion between ports A and B.

The pressure at which the valve opens and controls can be adjusted by altering the preload of the pilot valve spring

For use as a bypass or unloading valve as shown in Fig. 34(b), the connexions are the same as for a relief valve except that the control port C is connected to tank via a suitable valve.

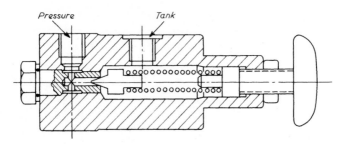

FIG. 33.—*Direct acting relief valve.*

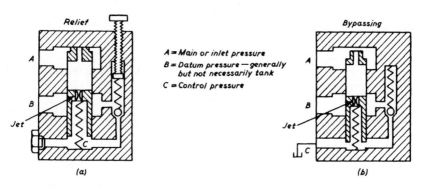

FIG. 34.—*Pilot operated relief valve.*

(b) *Reducing Valves*

These are used to limit the pressure in any particular portion of the circuit, and again may be of direct acting or pilot operated types.

Direct acting valves are used mainly for providing a low flow and reduced pressure for pilot operation of other valves and for certain types of remote or sequencing control.

Pilot operated units are used for greater flows, and to limit the pressure applied to certain equipment in the circuit. When used in conjunction with a suitable orifice, they may also be used to control or limit flow as well as pressure.

When used as a normal reducing valve, the direct acting type is very simple (Fig. 35). Main pressure is applied to Port B, Port A takes off the reduced pressure and Port C is connected to tank. Since a reducing valve is always held open by a spring, Port A and B are connected until the pressure in Port A overcomes the control spring, when the piston will move against the spring cutting off A from B.

The pilot operated reducing valve in Fig. 36 has the main piston retained in the open position by a light spring, and in the normal position ports A and B are connected. Main oil pressure enters at Port B, Port A being connected as the reduced pressure, Port C being connected permanently to tank.

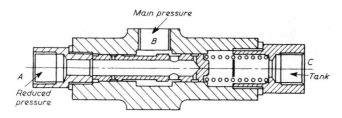

FIG. 35.—*Direct acting reducing valve.*

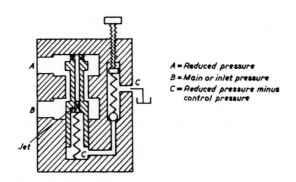

A = *Reduced pressure*
B = *Main or inlet pressure*
C = *Reduced pressure minus control pressure*

FIG. 36.—*Pilot operated reducing valve.*

As the pressure in A rises, it is commu   ated to the control chamber under the piston through the jet. When the pressure in the control chamber rises sufficiently to lift the pilot valve off its seat, flow takes place through the jet with a consequent pressure drop. The piston is now moved against the spring to throttle the flow of oil from B to A causing a reduced pressure at Port A.

Conversely, should the reduced pressure fall below that set by the pilot valve, the ball will seat allowing the spring to move the main piston to the open position, reducing the restriction and giving a corresponding increase in outlet pressure.

In this way, the valve restricts flow from ports B to A in order to maintain a constant pressure in the A port, whatever the supply pressure (B). Once again the "reduced" pressure level can be set by adjusting the spring load on the pilot valve.

3.12.4. Flow Control Valves

There are three main variants of this type of control.

(a) *Restrictor*

A simple needle valve, creating a variable restriction effectively controls flow if used as control valve A in Fig. 1(b). A significant disadvantage of this control however, is that the flow is directly dependent upon pressure, i.e. load and hence no unique relationship exists between valve opening and ram speed. With high pressures, accurate control of part speed conditions may be very difficult to achieve.

(b) *Bleed-off Flow Control*

The disadvantage mentioned above can be overcome by using a pilot operated valve as shown in Fig. 37. This valve is basically similar to the pilot operated relief valve described above and is used in conjunction with an orifice in the supply line.

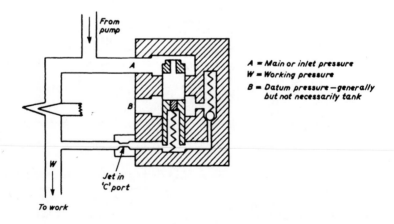

FIG. 37.—*Bleed-off flow control.*

For bleed-off flow control, the jet is moved from the piston and inserted in the port C purely for damping purposes. The tapped hole from which the jet was removed is then plugged. The port C is connected by a small bore (3–5 mm) pipe to the downstream side of an adjustable orifice. The inlet port of the orifice is connected to the pressure source and the outlet port to the work. Operation is similar to that of a relief valve, except that surplus oil is spilled off from Port B to tank. For any setting of the orifice, the resulting flow will be such that the pressures on either side of the orifice will be the same as those across the piston of the flow control valve. Should changes in the working pressure tend to alter the rate of flow, the piston will automatically move to a new position in which the original pressure drop and flow conditions are restored. Hence, the flow rate is not dependent upon working pressure level.

(c) *Series Flow Control*

The series flow control with orifice downstream (Fig. 38) functions in a similar way to the reducing valve. The pressure drop across the orifice is measured and transferred to the ends of the piston with due allowance for the control spring. Any variation in the flow through the orifice causes a variation in pressure drop across it and this, in turn, causes the main piston to take up a new position to restore the pressure drop and flow to the original settings.

The orifice may be a separate unit connected to the flow control valve by pipework, or it may be included in the design of the valve block as an integral unit. The orifice may be fixed or variable.

Series flow control valves are used where a number of operations have to be carried out from one pumping set. It is usually necessary to operate the pump at maximum pressure which is set by the relief valve. Some oil must constantly flow through this valve and since this flow—at maximum pressure—constitutes waste, power problems can arise through oil overheating.

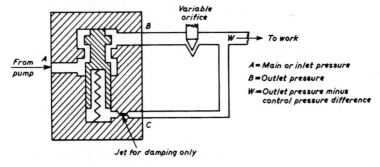

FIG. 38.—*Series flow control valve (orifice downstream).*

3.12.5. Sequence Valves

While these units are often classed with pressure control valves they are basically a directional control valve arranged to operate at a certain pressure, which is usually adjustable. They are intended, according to the requirement, to either open or close a secondary circuit during the cycle of operation.

Some units have an adjustable differential, particularly when used in conjunction with an accumulator unloading circuit.

3.12.6. Directional Control Valves

These valves, as their name implies, control the direction of flow of the fluid in the system, and are of three main types:
    a) Positive seated type in which a ball or piston moves on or off the seat;
    b) Rotary spool type in which the spool rotates about its own axis;
    c) Sliding spool type in which the spool moves axially in a bore; this is by far the most common arrangement and will therefore be considered in more detail.

Sliding spool type valves may be mechanically, manually, electrically or hydraulically operated, or even a combination of these. The principal geometries are shown in Table II. A very common arrangement is to have a solenoid operated valve as a pilot in order to operate a main valve hydraulically (Fig. 39). Directional control valves can have from two to six ports, although three and four are the most common. It is usual to give the number of positions of the spool and the number of flow paths provided in the extreme positions. For example, one which is very often used is a three-position, four-way valve which has two extreme and one central position, with two flow paths in each extreme position—making a total of four in all. Moving the spool or piston from one extreme position to the other reverses the connexions.

There are occasions when it may be necessary to hold the spool in a set position or even allow it to return to a set position after operation. Thus, detents are used for holding in fixed positions and springs, either spring offset or spring centred, to return the spool to a set position after operation.

The spool may have several forms according to the requirements of the circuit. For instance, it may be necessary to lock all ports in the centre position, or even lock the work ports while connecting the pressure port to tank. There are also occasions when all ports may be connected together in the centre position.

Whilst solenoid operated valves are widely used where electrical operation is required, the manually operated type is also common. In many applications several spools are required to operate a variety of circuits and banked valves have been developed which incorporate spools, relief valves and check valves in a single block. Figure 40 shows an example of such equipment.

FIG. 39.—*Two-stage solenoid operated directional spool valve.*

3.13. ACCUMULATORS

Examples of the two main types of accumulators commonly used in hydraulic circuits are shown in Figs 41 and 42.

In both types, a gas (usually nitrogen) is introduced into one chamber at a predetermined pressure which is chosen to give the required operating characteristics.

As the hydraulic system pressure rises above the pre-charge pressure, oil enters and displaces the piston or rubber bag. This reduces the gas volume and the pressure increases according to Boyle's Law

Pressure × Volume = Constant, at a constant temperature.

Oil continues to enter the accumulator until the maximum system pressure is reached. Since oil and gas are under virtually equal pressure, in the case of the piston type there is little tendency for leakage past the piston seal in either direction.

It is usual to select an accumulator of capacity slightly greater than the maximum required oil displacement. Piston type accumulators are usually used where large displacements are required and the effective gas volume can be increased by connecting the gas port to an external gas cylinder.

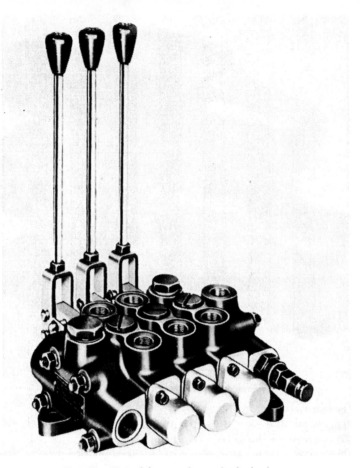

FIG. 40.—*Typical directional control valve bank.*

This reduces the compression ratio (maximum to pre-charge pressure).

A particular feature of the piston type shown in Fig. 42 is the fluid cut-off arrangement on the piston. As the circuit pressure falls and the oil discharges from the accumulator, the piston descends until the plunger enters the port, effecting a seal and trapping oil beneath the piston. Since this oil remains at high pressure whilst circuit pressures are low the pressure drop across the piston remains negligible and gas charge is therefore maintained without difficulty.

3.13.1. The Use of Accumulators

Accumulators are used to fulfil several roles in hydraulic circuits:

a) To maintain circuit pressure by compensating for pressure loss due to leakage or pressure increase due to rising temperature;

alternatively, in emergency conditions of power or pump failure, this may simply involve a holding pressure during shut down or the supply of adequate power to safely complete the operating cycle.

b) To absorb shock by cushioning circuit pressure rise as a result of sudden valve closure; or by cushioning transient pressure variations during start, stop or reversal of load movement; or by cushioning transient pressure from impact load variations.

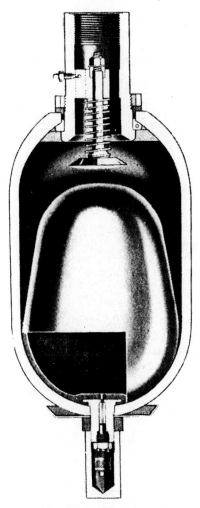

FIG. 41.—*Bag type accumulator.*
(Courtesy Fawcett Engineering Ltd.)

c) To supplement pump delivery where multiple circuit operations have wide flow variations with a short term peak demand in excess of pump capacity; accumulator charge can take place during low demand periods to meet maximum demand later.

d) To provide a high energy power source where there is high energy discharge after relatively long charging period, for, say, switchgear or valve operation.

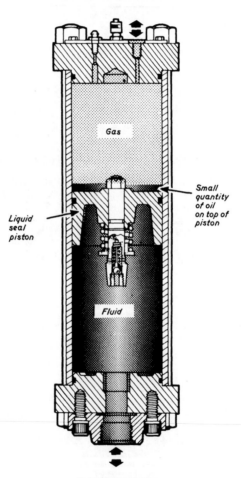

To gas bottle via suitable valves

Gas

Small quantity of oil on top of piston

Liquid seal piston

Fluid

To hydraulic system

FIG. 42.—*Piston type accumulator.*
(Courtesy Keelavite Hydraulics Ltd.)

TABLE II—SUMMARY OF A TYPICAL HYDRAULIC VALVE RANGE

Relief Valve PR
Normally used to limit system pressure to protect units. Pilot operated relief valve with balanced piston. A is connected to pressure and B normally but not essentially to tank. By connecting C2 port via a suitable control valve to tank, the pump flow can be returned to tank at a very low pressure, thereby saving wear on the pump.

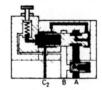

Reducing Valve PX
Used to limit the maximum pressure feed to a part of the circuit under all flow conditions. Pressure is fed to B port. The valve is normally open so that oil can pass freely from B to A until the reduced pressure setting is reached: at this point the piston is so regulated that the required reduced pressure output is not exceeded despite variations in supply pressure. The reduced pressure can be raised or lowered in value by adjustment of the knurled adjuster.

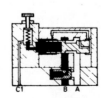

TABLE II—*continued.*

Reducing and Flow Control Valve PXE

Similar in operation to PX, but the jet is included between the working pressure line and the control chamber, either with a fixed orifice incorporated in the base-plate, or with a fixed or variable external orifice. This ensures both that the output pressure at A cannot exceed that set by the ad-juster, and also that the output flow rate through A cannot exceed the value determined by the size of the orifice, irrespective of the inlet or outlet pressures. It should be noted that whenever the pressure in the control chamber (i.e. the working pressure) lifts the pilot valve off its seat, the valve will not control flow but pressure.

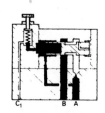

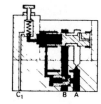

Relief Valve with External Jet PRE

Again similar in operation to PR except that the jet is included in the C2 line. This unit is used in conjunction with an external ori-fice, which may be fixed or variable, for bleed-off flow control duties.

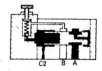

Sequence Valve PSOE

Essentially similar in operation to PSLE but normally open instead of closed, giving normally free flow A to B. Application of pilot pressure will close the valve and A and B are then locked.

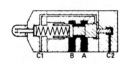

TABLE II—*continued.*

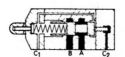

Sequence Valve PSLE
Normally closed, remotely controlled valve. For controlling sequence of oil flow. Application of pressure at C2 such that the force exerted on the piston is greater than the force exerted by the spring, will open the valve and connect A to B. A choice of springs is available so that the valve can be adjusted to open at any predetermined pilot pressure.

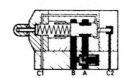

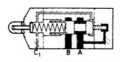

Sequence Valve PSLD
Normally closed directly operated pressure sequence valve. When pressure in the A port rises above the loading of the spring, the valve will open and A will be connected to B. Should the pressure fall at A the valve will close.

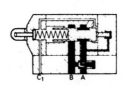

TABLE II—*continued.*

Sequence Valve PSOD
Similar to PSLD but normally open. When pressure A to B exceeds the spring setting the valve will close, locking A and B. When pressure at A drops below the spring setting the valve will once again open.

Unloading Valve PUL
Used in double pump systems to protect and offload the low pressure pump. Normally closed direct acting unloading valve. Application of pressure at port C2 in excess of spring loading will connect port A to port B. Port A is connected to pressure, and port B normally to tank. If pressure is removed from C2 the piston returns to its normal position under the influence of the spring, and ports A and B are locked.

Counterbalance Valve PCB
Similar in construction to PUL except that instead of a separate source of servo pressure the unloading pressure signal is taken from the A port. When this pressure signal exceeds the loading exerted on the piston by the spring, the valve will open and A will be connected to B, rather in the manner of a direct acting relief valve. This valve is used to counter act for biased loads, the load being connected to port A.

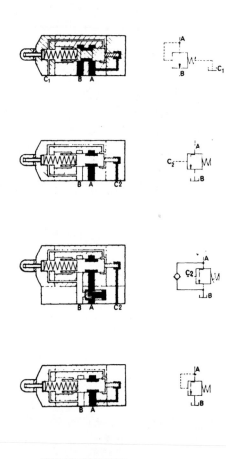

TABLE II—*continued.*

Variable Flow Control Valve
VFS
An extremely accurate, variable, series flow control valve. The accuracy of metering is unaffected by changes in viscosity. Used essentially for varying the speed of any hydraulic actuator within precise limits, irrespective of load. Micrometer type adjuster gives immediate indication of flow rate selected. Pressure is connected to port A, and port B is connected to the load.

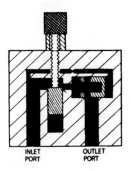

INLET PORT   OUTLET PORT

Direct Acting Check Valve CH
Free flow can take place through the valve A to B. Pressure at A will cause the piston to lift. When this pressure drops below the rating of the spring, or should pressure at B exceed pressure at A, the piston will re-seat.

Pilot Operated Check Valve CHP
Free flow can take place from A to B but reverse flow is prevented by the soft seat, unless pilot pressure is applied to port C_1, in which case free flow in both directions is possible.

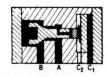

TABLE II—*continued.*

Manually Operated Directional Valve DH

Also available without hand lever for stem operation (DS). Four port directional valve. Choice of spool to give various port interconnexions in centre position. Two or three operating positions with choice of spring offset, spring centred, detent control or free spool.

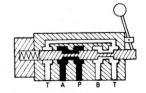

Pilot Operated Directional Valve DP

Pilot operated four port directional valve. Choice of spool as for DH. Valve is available with either two or three operating positions with choice of spring offset, spring centred, detent control or free spool. Tapped baseplate, including pilot connexions, to NFPA standards. Flows depending on valve size. Maximum pressure 210 bars (3000 lbf/in).

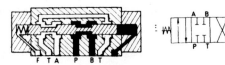

Solenoid Pilot Operated Directional Valve DE

Solenoid pilot operated four port directional valve. Choice of spool as for DH. Valve is available with either two or three operating positions with choice of spring offset, spring centred, detent control or free spool.

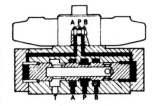

Solenoid Operated Directional Valve D- AC or D- DC

Four port solenoid operated directional valve essentially similar to DH and DS with similar choice of spool. Spool operation is by solenoid using AC or DC current. One or two solenoids may be used, depending on flow requirement from the unit, and the spool can be spring offset or spring centred.

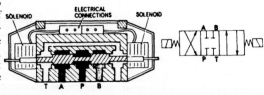

4. SOME PRACTICAL ASPECTS OF HYDRAULIC CIRCUITS

4.1. FILTRATION AND SYSTEM CLEANLINESS

The question of filtration and general cleanliness is one of the most difficult and controversial features of all hydraulic technology and remains probably the biggest single factor in "user education" towards hydraulic systems.

4.1.1. Basic Filter Construction

A filter is basically an arrangement which allows oil from the hydraulic circuit to pass through an element of metal, fibre or treated paper in order to remove debris present in the oil.

The varieties of design and applications range from relatively coarse metal mesh "strainers", often employed at both the oil tank filler and circuit off-take in the tank to stop larger particles and "objects" passing into the system (approximate "hole" size 100–150 microns (μm), see below), to high level filtration elements capable of stopping particles of 1 micron (1 μm).

Whatever the element used, the object is to achieve the maximum area presentation to the oil in order to reduce the oil velocities required for a given flow rate, and hence to minimize the pressure required to pass the oil through the filter. To achieve maximum area with minimum bulk in many designs the element is held in a convoluted cylindrical form with a sealed cap at either end, the detailed arrangement depending upon the element material.

The filter "bowl" carrying the element is designed to be readily removeable without disturbing the "head" with· the circuit pipe connexions, etc. to allow the element to be easily renewed as part of a regular maintenance procedure. (In the latest low pressure throwaway designs, the element and bowl consist of a one-piece assembly).

The siting of the filter in the circuit is discussed below but in general two types of filter body construction are available. Low pressure types are constructed to withstand pressures of some 20 bar (300 lbf/in^2) whereas filters for incorporation in high pressure areas of the circuit can withstand pressures of 350 bar (5000 lbf/in^2). An example is shown in Fig. 43.

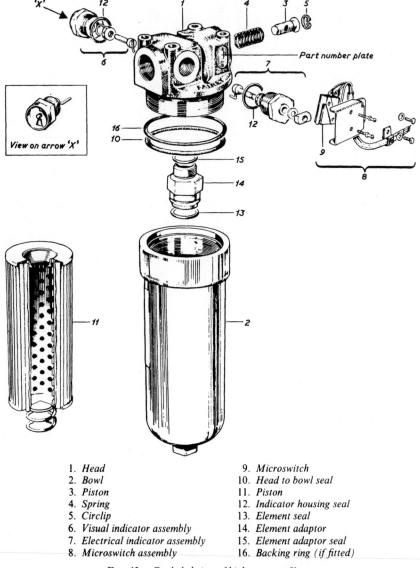

View on arrow 'X'

Part number plate

1. *Head*
2. *Bowl*
3. *Piston*
4. *Spring*
5. *Circlip*
6. *Visual indicator assembly*
7. *Electrical indicator assembly*
8. *Microswitch assembly*
9. *Microswitch*
10. *Head to bowl seal*
11. *Piston*
12. *Indicator housing seal*
13. *Element seal*
14. *Element adaptor*
15. *Element adaptor seal*
16. *Backing ring (if fitted)*

FIG. 43.—*Exploded view of high pressure filter.*

Usually, oil is fed to the outside of the element, passing through the material into the centre volume, which is connected to the outlet port. Obviously, as the filter removes the debris from the oil, the element pores gradually become blocked, gradually preventing progressively smaller particles from passing through. This accumulation thus progressively raises the pressure difference across the element required to pass the flow and ultimately, if no further action is taken, the element structure will collapse spilling debris back into the circuit and ending any filtering action. Of course, long before filter collapse occurs the increased pressure drop will be introducing an undesirable power loss into the system. The best method of preventing this situation and maintaining optimum filtration is to renew the filter element at regular intervals, but a by-pass is also provided as a safety measure. This is effectively a low pressure relief valve which opens to allow oil to pass from the inlet directly to the outlet of the filter when the pressure drop across the element has reached the maximum design value. With this arrangement, although no damage is done, with the by-pass open effective filtration is at an end until the element is renewed.

On many designs, filter condition indicators are fitted. A simple dial on the filter head indicates the relative level of pressure drop across the filter and hence its condition. In this way and with suitable markings, the time for filter renewal is clearly evident before the by-pass operates.

4.1.2. Filter Terminology

The standard unit of measurement in hydraulic filtration is the *micron*— a millionth part of a metre (1 μm).

Many different methods of indicating the filtering characteristics of an element material exist and many test methods are used to rate the material but the following two definitions of *Micron Rating* are in most common use.

(a) *Absolute Rating*

This is the physical size of the largest hole or pore in the filter material. It is difficult to measure and the 99 per cent efficiency point (see *Nominal Rating*) is often given as the Absolute Rating.

(b) *Nominal Rating*

A test curve is obtained showing the percentage of known size particles transmitted by a filter media (see Fig. 44). An arbitrary efficiency, typically 95 per cent is taken and the size particle stopped with this efficiency defines the nominal rating of the filter. Unfortunately, the arbitrary efficiency of the nominal rating is not always stated. (An important factor should be noted. Particles in excess of the filter rating will always be transmitted by the filter. Firstly, all particles are not spherical and when counted may present their largest diameter to the counting device having presented their minimum diameter to the filter. Secondly, pressure surges and pulses will distend material pore sizes and modify particle shapes).

(c) *"Pressure Drop"*

This is usually given as one figure for the whole filter, including the element. This pressure drop includes both case loss and element loss. Case losses are mainly dependent on the flow rate through the case, whilst element losses also vary noticeably with viscosity, i.e. fluid temperature. This latter factor can effect significantly the choice of filter size, particularly where wide temperature variations are likely, since at the lowest temperature, viscosity may be high enough to cause excessive pressure drop and open the by-pass.

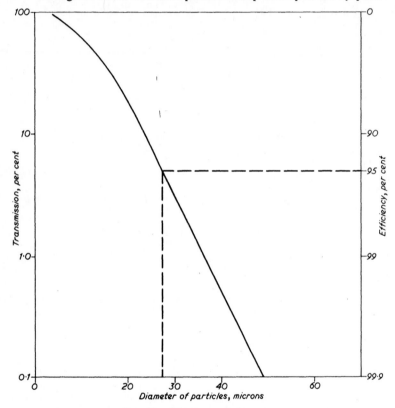

FIG. 44.—*Filter transmission curve.*

4.1.3. Filter Position
The following alternatives for siting filters have to be considered.

(a) *Inlet to Pump (Open Circuit)—Low Pressure*
Here, the main pump draws oil through the filter from the tank. This arrangement is not generally suitable since it is difficult to ensure an adequate size to avoid cavitation at the pump inlet.

With pumps requiring a boosted inlet, the above problem can be avoided by placing the filter between boost and main pump. The low pressure pump is unprotected, which is acceptable.

(b) *Return Line to Tank—Low Pressure*

Suitable for open circuit systems. No protection from self-generated debris or contamination of tank on topping up.

(c) *Pump Delivery—High Pressure*

Open or closed circuit. Full protection for circuit components after pump.

(d) *"Make-up" Line in Closed Circuit System*

Low pressure. No protection for main circuit self-generated debris. Generally found in piston pump transmission circuits. Filter between boost and main pump.

In practice, with open circuits return line filtration is the most widely used since low pressure filters only are required. However, with increasing system pressures and the consequent reduction in clearances in valves, a full flow filter on the outlet from the pump is being increasingly adopted from reliability and overall economy viewpoints.

A particular type of high pressure filter design, suitable for use with a reversing "closed circuit" transmission is shown in Fig. 45. This allows the fluid to pass through the element when the flow is in one direction, but automatically by-passes the element when flow is reversed. This prevents collected contaminant from re-entering the system.

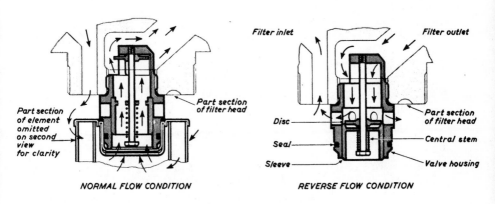

FIG. 45.—*Reverse flow filter by-pass arrangement.*
(Courtesy Fairey Filtration Ltd.)

With boosted piston pumps on either open or closed circuits, a low pressure filter between boost and main pump is ideal since the self-generated debris associated with this type of pump is negligible and the wear/leakage pattern within the pump ensures that any debris produced is washed into the drain back to tank and not retained within the system. In closed loop systems, this means the filter can be sized on "make-up" flow only which is a considerable advantage compared to open circuit requirements. Some designs of piston pump do in fact include integral valves which allow low pressure oil from the boost pump to flush through the low pressure lines of a closed circuit before flowing through the filter.

Generally, acceptable filtration levels for all equipment lie between 10 and 15 micron (μm) nominal rates. Although certain components can tolerate particles of debris above this size, it is certain that the improved filtration down to this level is reflected in a longer life with better performance.

However, with increased valve sophistication and the introduction of electrically operated servo valves, filtration requirements are likely to become more severe. In all cases, the fundamental factors involved with any filter—Area, Pressure Drop and Flow Throughput—have to be considered, and the cost penalty balanced against improved life and reliability.

4.2. Sources of Circuit Contamination

With reasonable and adequate cleanliness achievable through simple procedures, a hydraulic system is one of the most reliable forms of power transmission, but without this internal cleanliness aggravating, and costly, breakdowns can occur. It must be stressed at the same time that internal cleanliness is largely independent of the external environment. With adequate procedures, which are not considered excessive, hydraulic system reliability is readily achieved in filthy conditions encountered in steel making machinery, earthmoving and mining as well as the rather different but severe marine environment.

In any circuit debris may be present for the following reasons:
a) Inadequate preparation or accidental damage during construction of circuit pipe runs—especially likely where welding is involved;
b) Ingress of debris through the tank filler cap or from dismantling the system after initial commissioning;
c) Self-generated debris from the action of pumping and valve mechanisms.

The effects caused by (a) and (b) above can be minimized by taking particular care and carrying out thorough cleansing procedures on pipes and connectors before fitting. After any welding work, pickling, flushing and drying should be carried out as well as scratching, filing or grinding.

It is perhaps worthwhile to point out that system contamination can be influenced significantly by the correct positioning of critical circuit components. If filters are easy to remove, regular maintenance procedures are encouraged.

Oil tank filler caps, etc. will probably not be adequately wiped during topping up, so that if a position can be found which is protected from the environment, the chance of serious contamination is reduced. Pipe runs which are of an efficient design and which have well positioned components also ease the task of replacement.

4.3. Commissioning Procedures

In every case, it is worthwhile considering the commissioning procedure to be adopted for removing the initial relatively high levels of debris which are inevitably included. A little extra time and trouble at this stage can ensure years of trouble free operation. Assuming contamination of all parts of the circuit, it may be worthwhile connecting extra filters into the circuit for a short period whilst system operation is checked.

Under all circumstances, the circuit should be operated repeatedly at low pressure and power levels throughout its entire cycle to ensure that a thorough flushing is achieved whilst the filter condition is closely watched. This period also of course allows time to check for external oil leaks, etc. After commissioning is complete, or before if seen to be necessary, the filter elements should be changed.

Assuming adequate precautions during construction and commissioning the long term performance of the system may depend on the siting of the permanent filters.

4.4. Cooling

In many cases, particularly where lower powered open circuits are concerned, a separate oil cooler is not required to dissipate the power losses which are manifest as heat in any hydraulic circuit. Full advantage should be taken of the oil tank which is required to meet circuit capacity variations and the optimum tank siting should be chosen to maximize heat dissipation. Of course, natural dissipation occurs from pipe runs and cylinder surfaces, etc. However, with higher powers, oil-to-air, or oil-to-water heat exchangers are usually required. Since suitable equipment is usually "low pressure" only, and since performance improves with increased oil temperature, the siting in the return to tank line is usually adopted.

With totally enclosed piston pumps in closed circuits, where the pump body contains low pressure "leakage" oil, the boost relief valve "exhaust" can be passed through the pump body to the cooler to increase heat dissipation.

4.5. Tank Design

The effective design and positioning of the oil tank can have an important influence on the successful operation of the circuit and, indeed, on the life of the circuit components. Poor tank design can result in frothing, cavitation and oil deterioration.

The object of tank design should be to allow oil to remain in the tank for the maximum length of time. To ensure this, the return pipes—which must at all times terminate below the oil surface—should be positioned as far as possible from the outlet. The outlet itself should be low in the tank but with a short stand pipe. A weir or angled baffle reduces oil velocity and allows time for any foam to disperse.

5. SOME TYPICAL APPLICATIONS OF HYDRAULIC TRANSMISSION

The applications of hydraulic drive on board different types of ships are too various to be covered in detail; it is hoped that the previous sections will have provided both interesting and useful information which can be related to differing circumstances and requirements. Finally, therefore, consideration will be given to a few particular areas where hydraulics are utilized.

5.1. DECK CRANES AND WINCHES

The use of hydrostatic drives in cranes, winches and similar equipment has grown considerably over the years until it is now accepted as a conventional method of drive in many cases.

The makers of ships' deck machinery were probably the pioneers in using low speed, low pressure equipment. The impetus for this is the freedom of installation resulting from the lack of mechanical connexions between prime mover and the machinery, as well as the important safety feature of the high pressure relief valve limiting the maximum motor output torque—thus safeguarding the winch mechanism and cable from overloading.

These fundamental advantages are equally applicable today. However, great progress has been made in the use of low cost equipment used at higher speeds and pressures, and a wide range of valve gear has made possible the use of reliable, highly sophisticated systems, e.g. with integrated override controls, remote controls and horsepower limiting controls. It is in the field of control that the greatest strides have been made in recent years, and this, coupled with the continuing evolution and detailed development of the basic pumps and motors, has improved both the performance measured in absolute terms, and the all important response to the operator's hand or foot movements. An example of a modern hydraulic deck crane is shown in Fig. 46.

5.1.1. Performance Requirements

(a) *Hoist*

In any winching system, the hoist winch motor probably has the most exacting duty to perform; apart from covering the speed

76

range up to the maximum light hook speed, the low speed performance is extremely critical. The motor must start from rest smoothly and accelerate in a controllable manner, the most demanding case being when restarting to lift the maximum suspended load. Here, the motor must develop the maximum output torque when at rest, possibly with metal to metal contact between the dynamic elements, giving higher friction than when rotating with established hydrodynamic oil films.

Since leakage normally reduces as speed increases, the minimum stable speed is governed by the ratio between maximum and minimum leakage within the cycle of one rotation; motors with a high static leakage tend to start suddenly and have a high minimum speed. This minimum speed plays a major part in determining the extent of any dead band in control response around the neutral position, and is a critical factor governing the all-important inching and general control response of any hydrostatic transmission.

FIG. 46.—10-*ton hydraulic deck cranes.*
(Courtesy Stothert and Pitt Ltd.)

The wide range of high torque, low speed motors described earlier are available for driving winch drums directly so dispensing with the need to fit reduction gearing. Motors of this type are more common on larger cranes where reduction gearboxes would be expensive. The saving in gearbox cost is to some extent offset by the fact that the brake must withstand full drum torque plus a safety overload, and must therefore be relatively large.

All fixed capacity motors, whether high or low speed, require a high flow at low pressure to obtain high light hook speeds and consequent short cycle times. With large cranes this can become an embarrassment and one solution with low speed motors is to use the two speed type where half the cylinders can be isolated hydraulically from an auxiliary circuit, so doubling the speed and halving the output torque from a given flow and pressure.

With a radial piston motor of this type it is also possible to utilize a rotating outer casing as the inner member of a band brake to give an attractive solution (Fig. 47).

High speed motors with reduction gearing have the advantage that the brake can be mounted on the high speed shaft and so be much smaller and cheaper. Because of the availability of standard low cost gearboxes this arrangement is popular on lighter cranes.

FIG. 47.—*Deck winch installation with a slow speed high torque motor and integral band brake on outer casing.*
(Courtesy Hägglund and Söner AB)

Variable capacity axial piston motors have the important advantage that light hook speeds can be increased up to four times from a given oil flow by reducing the motor capacity to 25 per cent of the maximum.

(b) *Luff*

If a luffing winch is used, the requirements are similar to those of the hoist winch. The maximum load position is determined by the geometrical layout of the crane.

Alternatively, hydraulic cylinders can be used for luffing and in this case it is necessary to fit two-way-acting, counterbalance valves to prevent untoward movement of the jib which may occur by either creeping under load or rapid movement caused by tension in the hoisting ropes.

(c) *Slew*

The slewing duty is particularly arduous as the mass of the superstructure has to be accelerated, and brought back to rest at each cycle. Unless the motor is operated by a variable capacity pump with a damped response, it will normally be necessary to operate on the relief valve during both acceleration and deceleration.

Adequate torque is required to slew on a cross slope caused by an unbalanced cargo during loading or unloading of a ship.

A by-pass across the slew motor is also needed to act as an anti-swing device; the low polar moment of inertia of the rotating parts of a hydraulic motor allowing the mass of the superstructure to oscillate out of phase with the load—damping the swing. In this case, the bypass valve would normally be foot operated and spring loaded to the closed position.

5.1.2. Safety Features

(a) *Braking*

The requirement here is for a system that will hold any load securely, allow a smooth changeover from static to winding or vice versa, and will fail safe, i.e. on at all times.

The normal procedure is to use a brake which is spring loaded to the "on" position and which is retracted by a hydraulic or air cylinder. The fluid supply to the cylinder can then be controlled by a single solenoid three-way valve with its spool again spring loaded to the "brake on" position to guard against electrical failures.

The signal to operate the brake can be taken from a micro switch on the control lever.

(b) *Override Controls*

Over-ride controls are normally required to prevent damage or operation in unsafe areas, e.g. slew angle, maximum and minimum luff angle, over-hoist protection (to prevent the hook lifting the jib) and slack rope protection (to prevent tangling, taking a rope tension signal from a dancing roller). The most convenient method is to use electrical signals from micro switches on the various solenoid valves which operate the movements, but in some applications where this could be unsafe, e.g. deck machinery on a tanker, a fully hydraulic system can be used with cam operated spool valves replacing the micro switches.

One successful method of using these limit signals has been to operate the stroke control of a variable capacity pump from a lever system with a collapsible pivot which is held rigid by oil pressure. Operation of an over-ride trip exhausts the pressure and effectively disconnects the operator's hand lever from the stroke control. The pump control itself is fitted with centralizing springs which bring the pump automatically to the zero flow position and apply the brake.

Where necessary, the linkage can be arranged such that the motion concerned can be returned to its normal range by the operator, but not taken further past the stop.

5.1.3. Variable Pump Systems

Part of a typical variable capacity pump system is shown in Fig. 48, the complete system comprising three such circuits for hoist, luff and slew drives. The circuit consists of a variable capacity axial piston pump, with the ability to reverse the direction of oil flow by overcentre operation of the swashplate. The swashplate is moved by an integral jack fitted with a follow up servo valve to isolate the actuator from the swashplate reaction forces, and to reduce the force required on the capacity control to a minimum.

The pump and fixed capacity motor are connected by the main flow pipes to form a closed circuit transmission system.

The brake cylinder is operated by boost pressure through a solenoid valve which is shown in the energized position releasing the brake. The valve is controlled such that it is de-energized when the pump swashplate control is at zero delivery. The switch is also operated over a small band about the zero position in order to prevent momentary load creep due to leakage in the pump and motor when starting a heavy load from rest.

With this system, the brake is applied automatically should the boost pressure fail for any reason, e.g. low oil level in the tank, burst hoses, fractured pipe fittings in the boost or main circuits, or failure of the main pump or motor. As an additional precaution, an emergency stop button can be fitted to apply all brakes irrespective of the pump stroke control settings.

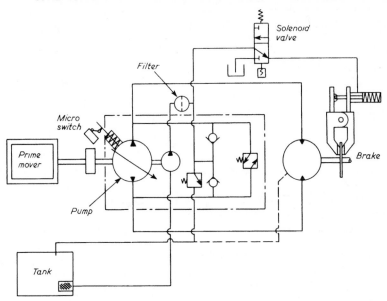

FIG. 48.—*Crane circuit for hoist, luff or slew drive using a variable capacity piston pump.*
(Courtesy Lucas Industrial Equipment Ltd.)

The pump stroke control is fitted with a spring centring system, so that if any handle is released, the motion stops automatically and the brake is applied. For this purpose, the spring centring and servo system must have a positive action with zero hysteresis to eliminate creep and any tendency to drive against the brake. The response of the servo system should also be rapid enough to give instant response to the operator's command signals, particularly when stopping the winch in an emergency. Experience in this field has shown that the use of high pressure oil from the main circuit to power the servo jack is particularly advantageous in ensuring a consistent servo response under all operational conditions, adequate power being always available as the swashplate reaction forces increase with pressure in the main circuit. An example of such a servo arrangement is shown earlier in Fig. 19.

For shipboard installations a continuously running electric motor imposes a smaller electrical load on the ship's generator than hoists with independent electric motors, particularly as the motor can be started against a negligible load with all the pumps at zero flow.

Systems of the type described give infinitely variable speed control in both directions with very good inching characteristics. They also possess the ability to operate all three motions simultaneously but independently, with a high overall efficiency, as power generated during lowering is fed back into the prime mover rather than being dissipated as heat in the oil in counterbalance valves which are necessary with fixed displacement pumps and open circuit systems.

5.1.4. Power Controls

The above variable pump system is adequate where the installed horsepower of the prime mover is capable of meeting the "corner horsepower" condition, i.e. driving all pumps at full flow and full pressure which in some instances can be a design requirement for a crane. In some cases, however, the power available may be limited either by lack of a suitable supply or economic design considerations and an override power control, particularly on the hoist pump, can be desirable to prevent the operator overloading the prime mover. A control of this type is shown in Fig. 49.

The pump with servo controlled swashplate is as previously described, but with a "soft link" mechanism interposed between the push pull servo valve control and the input from the operator's handle. The power override consists of a cylinder with a piston which is pushed outwards by a pressure signal from the hoist pressure side of the circuit. The piston is returned by a spring or springs calibrated to give a close approximation to the theoretical relationship for constant input horsepower at a given drive speed,

$$Flow \times Pressure = Constant$$

Piston extension moves a stop which restricts the movement of the swash angle control and the "soft link" collapses if the operator selects too high a flow rate (see also Table I).

Power controls of this type give a close approximation to the theoretical power input, are simple, rugged, and have performed most reliably in service.

5.1.5. Fixed Displacement Pump Systems

Fixed displacement gear or vane type pumps for medium pressure up to 175 bar (2500 lbf/in^2) will operate at high speeds without the pressurized inlet often required by piston pumps and are, therefore, extremely popular on applications where their lower efficiency can be tolerated.

The pump simplicity is offset to some extent by the fact that control problems have to be overcome in other parts of the circuit, but these are invariably solved by the aid of multi-bank spool valves which are available at low cost. A typical crane valve would consist of a supply pressure relief valve operative on all circuits followed by three open centred spool valves connected in parallel to the oil supply. Each spool would have a neutral mid-position to which it was biased by a centralizing spring.

A hand lever on each spool offsets the valve to give oil flow in either direction to the two service ports connected to the motor or ram. Each spool has a check valve in its supply port to prevent a reverse flow of oil

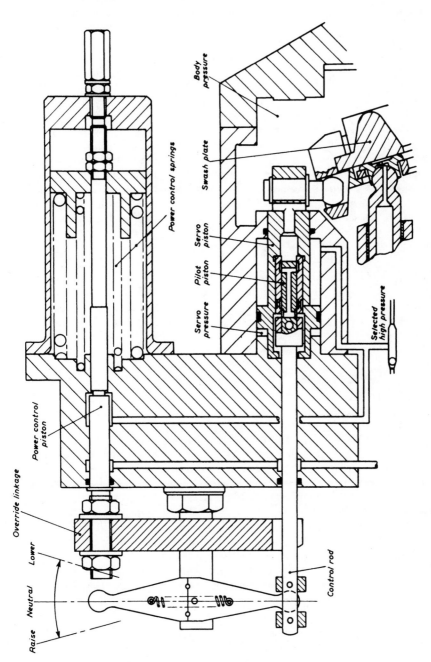

FIG. 49.—*Variable pump control for power limiting.*

should the spool be opened when the pressure in the service line is higher than the supply pressure available—for example, when a second service is being operated at a lower pressure by another spool.

The spools are fitted with metering darts, or tapers, to give gradual opening or closing in proportion to the lever movement, so giving the operator a degree of speed control in addition to that obtained by varying the speed of the prime mover where appropriate. Additional service line relief valves are available to protect the system from overloads caused by inertia and structural loads when the valve spools are closed to the service lines, e.g. when decelerating a rotating superstructure in the latter part of the slewing cycle. A closed circuit piston pump system will hold a load by hydraulic lock when the pump is on a low displacement, but this is not possible with gear or vane pump open circuit systems and counterbalance valves are needed to control the lowering of a load on the luff and hoist motions. This results in heat generation as the power is dissipated into the oil, which must then be cooled.

5.2. Ring Main Systems

In certain applications, where several items of equipment have to be operated at different times, the provision of individual prime movers and pumps would be uneconomic. A typical application would be a bulk tanker, which could require hydraulic operation of cargo pumps, valves, cranes, and winches.

The most common solution is to use at a central pumping station a number of variable-capacity pressure-compensated pumps feeding a high pressure manifold, which is used as a ring main to supply all the hydraulic services on the vessel.

The number of pumps is matched to the peak load and they can be switched on or off automatically as the demand varies.

The electrical load can be reduced by venting the pressure controls, such that the pumps start on no load and should a pump be damaged it can be replaced without stopping the rest of the system.

The flow from the ring main to each individual service is controlled by a fixed or variable, pressure-compensated, flow control valve depending on the duty required. Any circuits downstream from this valve are similar to those for fixed displacement pumps with the exception that the controlling spool valves are of the closed centre type, stopping flow in the neutral position which would otherwise waste power across the flow control valve.

An alternative supply to the pressure compensated, variable capacity pumps is to use multiple fixed capacity pumps and flow switching valves as described in Section 1.4.

5.3. Windlasses and Capstans

The typical hydraulic windlass and capstan installation shown in Fig. 50 uses fixed capacity pumps and slow speed high torque motors,

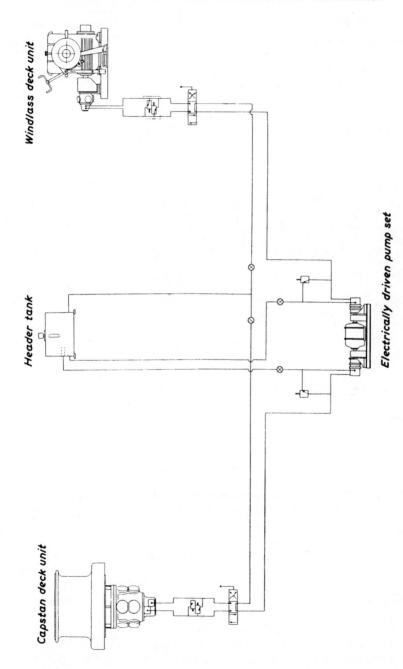

FIG. 50.—Piping arrangement for hydraulic windlass and capstan installation.

controlled through manually operated directional spool valves. The capstan unit is designed with the motor mounted directly beneath the drum, thus dispensing with gearing and allowing the motor to be conveniently underslung below deck.

The electric motor driven pump set can similarly be positioned below deck.

Such a system provides high torque with low moments of intertia to cut acceleration times, whilst overloads are prevented through the protection provided by the high pressure relief valves. Figure 51 shows a typical windlass deck unit.

FIG. 51.—*Winch windlass on a modern dredger.*

(Courtesy K & L Marine Equipment Ltd.)

5.4. CONSTANT TENSION WINCHES

A variation of the constant pressure and constant horsepower control for variable capacity pumps is used to achieve constant tension winch systems. In this case the pump control is automatically operative across neutral such that constant system pressure and hence a constant motor torque/winch tension is maintained whilst both drawing in and paying out.

5.5. CARGO VALVE ACTUATION

The actuation of liquid bilge and ballast cargo valves is an important application of hydraulics in modern marine engineering practice. Systems can involve the actuation and monitoring of between 100 and 200 valves of various types. Local control at the valve station, powered from a ring main system can be provided, but more usually such systems involve central power generation, control, and monitoring.

Valve operations are controlled from a central control console on which the condition (open, part open or closed) of each power operated valve is indicated on a mimic diagram which depicts the complete pipework and pumping system of the ship. A typical schematic layout is shown in Fig. 52. With this type of system the complete unloading, loading and ballasting programmes of modern complex liquid carriers can be controlled to ensure minimum turn-round times and involving the minimum man-power.

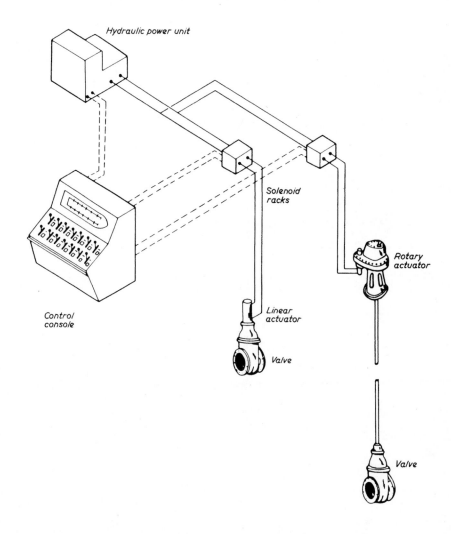

FIG. 52.—*Typical cargo valve actuating system—schematic arrangement.*

5.5.1. Rotary Actuator

An example of the rotary type of valve actuator is shown in Fig. 53. In this, a compact high torque hydraulic motor drives the valve shaft through suitable reduction gearing.

An important feature of a rotary actuator is the in-built automatic control. The full output torque must be available to break the valve out of its seat, yet it is essential that a wedge gate valve is driven into its seat with

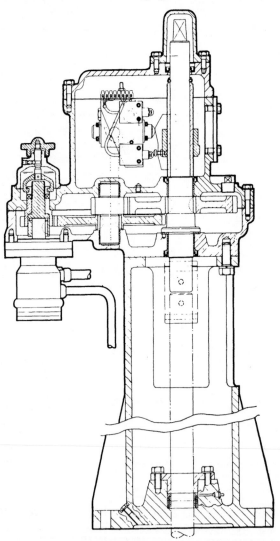

FIG. 53.—*Rotary hydraulic actuator with deck stand and gas seal.*
(Courtesy Hydraulics and Pneumatics Ltd.)

a lower torque. Part of the energy available to drive the valve home is the kinetic energy of the rotational system from motor to valve. Large valves require heavy reach rods and relatively high actuator speeds. The inertia to be absorbed when stopping the system can be substantial and could easily force the valve so hard into its seat as to make re-opening by the actuator impossible. To reduce this tendency, the automatic control reduces the output torque of the actuator during the closing stages and reduces the speed of the actuator at the same time. A 50 per cent speed reduction causes a 75 per cent reduction in inertia which generally makes inertia effects negligible.

Torque reduction is effected by reducing the effective hydraulic pressure across the driving motor to a figure suitably below system pressure, and speed reduction is effected by throttling the flow of hydraulic fluid.

These operations are initiated concurrently within a single control unit built into the actuator casing (see Fig. 54). The sequence, starting from the fully closed valve position is:

1) At command "Valve Open" the actuator develops maximum torque (dependent on system pressure) at reduced speed;

2) After approximately 3 turns of the actuator (approximately 10 per cent of valve movement), it continues at maximum torque but increases to full speed;

3) Approximately 3 turns before the "fully open" position, the hydraulic supply to the drive motor is cut off and motion stops;

4) At command "Valve Close" the actuator develops reduced torque at reduced speed;

5) After approximately 3 turns it develops maximum torque and increases to full speed;

6) Approximately 3 turns before the "fully closed" position it reduces both speed and torque;

7) As the wedge seals into its seat, the actuator is stalled by the valve resistance. Until the hydraulic supply is switched off, the motor continues to develop the reduced torque under stalled conditions.

Local mechanical indicators of valve position are normally fitted and, in addition, electric or pneumatic remote indication can be provided. The optional command alternatives include local hydraulic, remote hydraulic, remote electro–hydraulic and remote pneumo–hydraulic.

5.5.2. Semi-Rotary Actuator—Rack and Pinion

This type of actuator (Fig. 55) operates butterfly, plug and ball valves with up to 90° rotation from open to closed.

The unit shown is suitable for both submerged and non-submerged operations.

The 90° rotation is achieved through a rack and pinion. Linear motion of the rack is produced by pistons fitted on each end and moving in cylinders on both sides of the actuator casing. An important feature of this type of unit is the ability to hydraulically lock the piston in any position, i.e. maintain a partially closed valve position.

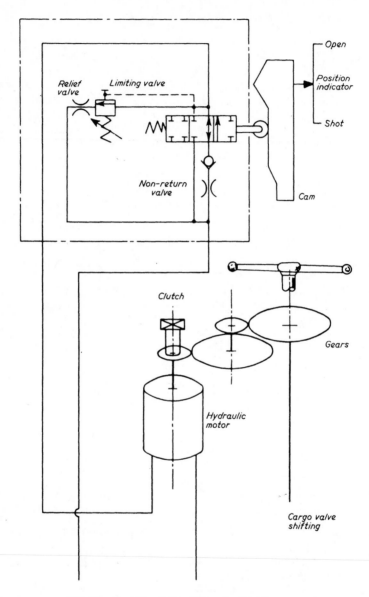

FIG. 54.—*Control unit circuit for valve actuation sequencing.*
(Courtesy Hydraulics and Pneumatics Ltd.)

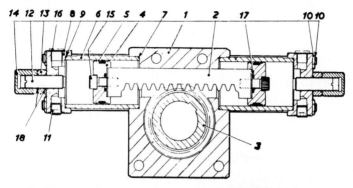

1. *Cast iron casing*
2. *Steel rack*
3. *Steel pinion*
4. *Steel piston*
5. *Synthetic rubber piston seal*
6. *Steel cylinder*
7. *Synthetic rubber O-rings as cylinder end seals*
8. *Steel and caps*
9. *Synthetic rubber O-rings as end cap seals*
10. *Steel tie rods with brass nuts*
11. *Brass end cap plug*
12. *Steel position adjusting screws*
13. *Brass locknut*
14. *Brass cap nut*
15. *Steel piston retaining screw*
16. *Plastic transit plug*
17. *Synthetic rubber O-ring as piston rack seal*
18. *Synthetic rubber O-ring as adjusting screw seal*

FIG. 55.—*Section through rack and pinion valve actuator.*

5.5.3. Worm and Wheel Actuator (Fig. 56)

Again a high torque low speed motor is used to drive the worm which in turn rotates the toothed wheel fitted to the valve shaft.

5.5.4. Linear Actuator (Fig. 57)

This is simply a double acting ram attached to the operating rod of a parallel slide valve.

5.6. CHEMICAL PUMP DRIVES

Two examples of chemical pump assemblies are shown in Fig. 58 and 59. In both cases, a hydraulic motor is mounted directly to the pump stand. Such equipment is typical of that which can conveniently be supplied from a ring main with either remote or local control through flow control valves.

Alternatively, the pump motor may be supplied directly from hydraulic pumps located in a pump room in the machinery space. In either case the cargo pump speed can easily be adjusted by controlling the input hydraulic oil flow to the drive motor to accommodate cargoes of different specific gravity.

5.7. STEERING GEAR

The hydraulic operation of steering gear involves both standard and specialized equipment.

FIG. 56.—*Worm and wheel rotary actuator.*
(Courtesy Hamworthy Engineering Ltd.)

The hydraulic power supply is obtained from a standard hydraulic pump driven either by electric motor or by power take off; system design, filtration standards, etc. will be typical. In the majority of cases the final rudder actuation is through heavy duty cylinders.

However, the control elements include either special telemotor units, basically similar to standard hydraulic piston pumps and motors, and associated servo valves to control power, or electrical transmitters and servos to proportion flow for rudder actuation.

Particular circuits to achieve hand and power steering and automatic pilot facility are shown in Fig. 60. Figures 61 and 62 show examples of cylinder and rotary steering units and an example of a valve power control unit is illustrated in Fig. 63.

For power steering, the telemotor is hand operated by the wheel and the oil flow positions a spool in the power control unit to feed oil proportionately to rudder cylinders from the power unit. A mechanical link, which is

FIG. 57.—*Linear actuator for wedge gate valves.*
(Courtesy Hydraulics and Pneumatics Ltd.)

positioned by rudder rotation, provides mechanical feedback into the control unit to interrupt the cylinder supply when the rudder angle corresponds to that demanded by the telemotor input.

Suitable hydraulic by-passes are fitted to allow direct manual operation, and as in other applications, relief valves prevent over-stressing—which in this case can result from shocks due to heavy weather. (The rudder returns to the original position after the relief valves have opened.)

With this type of system it is thus possible to have an instant rudder response to the slightest movement of the wheel, and since wheel movement only moves the control spool via the telemotor pump, then only a small number of effortless turns are required hard over to hard over when power steering is operative.

A hand lever on the power control valve assembly allows for local power hydraulic steering and hand steering is available automatically at all times by means of an automatic valve in the event of a power failure or stopped power pumps.

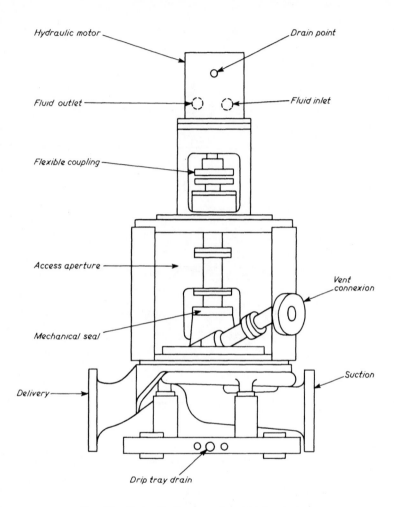

FIG. 58.—*Hydraulically powered vertical chemical pump.*
(Courtesy Hamworthy Engineering Ltd.)

5.8. DREDGING

Hydraulic power transmission has been successfully applied to most forms of dredgers. Suction dredgers employ hydraulics to position the suction tube, cutter dredgers have hydraulic motors fitted to the cutter drive, and bucket dredgers have hydraulic drive to the bucket chain. In addition, hydraulics is used to power winches and capstans, and to provide remote control of various valves and doors.

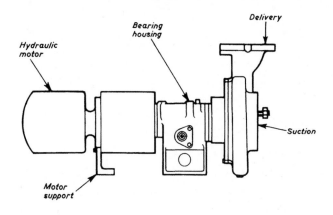

FIG. 59.—*Hydraulically powered horizontal chemical pump.*
(Courtesy Hamworthy Engineering Ltd.)

5.8.1. Suction Dredger

In the trailing suction dredger, hydraulic drives may be fitted for winches, capstans, sluice valves, overside suction pipe operation, launder or suction passage doors, bottom doors and cotters and steering gear.

5.8.2. Winches

These are usually in two classes: those required for normal lifting or manoeuvring duties and those concerned with the lifting of the overside suction pipe. The former are operated by a simple hydraulic circuit in which the hydraulic motor is reversed and controlled for speed by a valve or variable displacement pump as described earlier. Working pressures are frequently of the order of 70 bar (1000 lbf/in^2) with peak pressures at starting in the range 125–140 bar (1800–2000 lbf/in^2). Some means of braking is usually required as described for parking or holding a suspended load.

5.8.3. Overside Pipes

The control of the overside pipe presents a more complex problem as it can involve the use of three winches which may be operated simultaneously, or independently.

5.8.4. Suction Head

In order to maintain the suction head in the correct position when the ship is rolling, arrangements are made to allow for the shortening or lengthening of the winch cables. This may be achieved by interposing between the winch and the pipe a large hydraulic cylinder of single-acting type fed by an

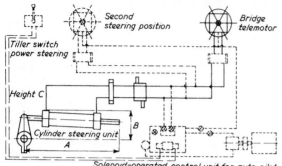

Solenoid-operated control unit for auto-pilot
control or power-assisted steering

*Typical piping diagram of a
hand hydraulic steering gear
indicating the alternative
second steering position
and the solenoid operated
control unit with control
pump to allow operation by
means of an automatic pilot
and/or power steering from
a lever type tiller switch.
Cylinder arrangements can
be given for twin rudder
installations*

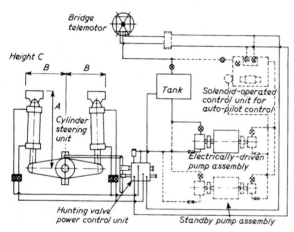

*Typical piping diagram of a
hand and power hydraulic
steering gear with one
electrically driven power
pump when emergency hand
hydraulic steering would
automatically be available at
the steering wheel in the
event of a power failure.
The alternatives show a
second electrically driven
power pump when
emergency hand hydraulic
steering is not essential and
a solenoid operated control
unit to allow operation by
means of an automatic pilot
and/or a lever type tiller
switch. Cylinder
arrangements can be given
for twin rudder installations.*

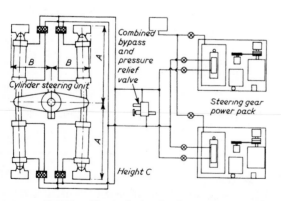

*Typical piping diagram of a
power hydraulic steering
gear arranged with two
power packs to allow
operation from an electric
steering control system
incorporating automatic
pilot. In the event of
damage to one of the
cylinders, any pair of
steering gear cylinders can
be isolated to allow two
cylinders to operate the
rudder instead of the usual
four.
Cylinder arrangements can
be given for twin rudder
installations.*

FIG. 60.—*Circuits for hand and power steering with automatic pilot facility.*

(*Courtesy K & L Marine Equipment Ltd.*)

FIG. 61.—*Cylinder steering units.*
(Courtesy K & L Marine Equipment Ltd.)

hydraulic accumulator. Figure 64 illustrates this in a simplified form. The cable from the winch drive is fed through a system of pulleys, one or more of which are mounted at the end of the piston rod of the hydraulic cylinder, and then over the pulley or pulleys on the gantry. Oil from the accumulator

is fed to the full area side of the cylinder and the pressure in the cylinder is
set to be sufficient for the suction pipe to maintain the piston rod in the
retracted position. As soon as the load is taken off the cable, when the head
touches the sea bed, the piston rod can extend to take up the slack, but as
the vessel rolls away from the head, the piston rod retracts against the pressure

FIG. 62.—*Rotary steering unit.*
(Courtesy K & L Marine Equipment Ltd.)

FIG. 63.—*Valve control unit.*
(Courtesy K & L Marine Equipment Ltd.)

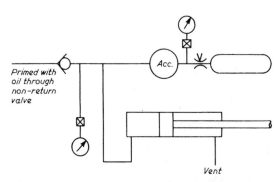

FIG. 64.—*Hydraulic circuit for swell compensator.*
(Courtesy Keelavite Hydraulics Ltd.)

in the cylinder and accumulator to take up its original position with the cable taut. Since the rise and fall of the head can be as much as 6m, a system of sheaves is sometimes necessary, so enabling a shorter cylinder to be used.

A relief valve is placed between the two main units and a hand pump may be used for filling the system. Alternatively, where there are other hydraulic circuits on board, one of these may be tapped for the purpose. An easily visible pressure gauge is required for the skipper to check that the swell compensating system is functioning correctly.

5.8.5. Valves

In order to maintain efficient operation with the minimum of crew, the valves which control the discharge overboard or into the well are often hydraulically operated.

5.8.6. Bottom Doors/Hopper Doors/Cotters

These rely on hydraulic cylinders for opening, closing and holding, either for long or short periods.

In some ships, mechanical cotters are omitted and a high pressure is maintained on the door rams to keep the doors closed, even when fully loaded. The doors are raised to their seats using a large volume low-pressure pump which is then unloaded and a small volume high-pressure pump is used to keep the doors closed. An accumulator may also be used with advantage to hold the doors closed when not working or in an emergency. An example of a circuit is shown in Fig. 65.

5.8.7. Cutter Dredger

On one cutter dredger the twin contra-rotating cutters are driven by two separate and independent hydraulic motors each developing 224 kW (300 hp) at 650 rev/min. Each cutter motor has its own self-contained circuit, but in order to provide power to operate the ladder hoist, one circuit is modified so that the pump may be used either to power the cutter or to operate the winch motors.

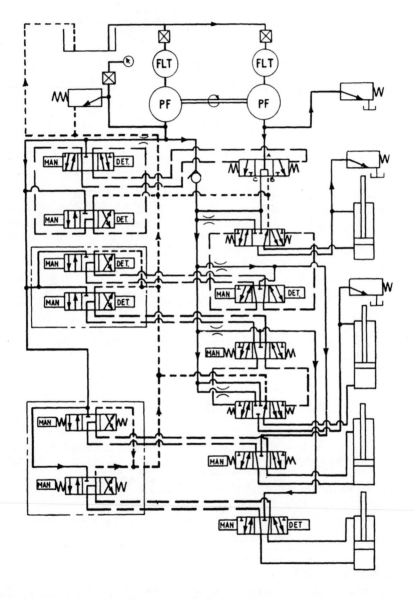

FIG. 65.—*Hydraulic circuit for hopper door operation.*

The circuit for the combined system is shown in Fig. 66. The cutter drive takes the form of a variable capacity pump, capable of being moved over centre to provide reversal of the drive, and a fixed capacity hydraulic motor. Both these units are of the axial piston type. To switch the pump flow from the cutter motor to the ladder winch, or vice versa, a double solenoid operated pilot valve is used to signal the switch over of a directional valve, the operator selecting the motion required.

The ladder winch uses the variable capacity pump to drive four radial piston hydraulic motors, and in order to prevent the bias loading of the ladder causing the motors to run away, a counterbalance valve is fitted with non-return valve to allow free return. The counterbalance valve is set at a pressure which will just hold the ladder in position, allowing for maximum torque. In these circumstances, if for any reason power should fail, the ladder will move slowly downwards—because of the internal leaks of the motors and counterbalance valve—until the brake is applied.

The speed of the cutter is controlled from the bridge by means of two handwheels, that of the ladder winch by a single lever at a point on the bridge adjacent to the cutter control, or alternatively, by another lever at a point on deck adjacent to the ladder.

The remote control of pump capacity is achieved hydraulically with cylinder operation of the integral pump control.

5.8.8. Bucket Dredger

Bucket dredgers, in addition to their equipment which is common to the suction and cutter dredgers, may also have an hydraulic drive for the bucket chain since there are several advantages to such a drive. The hydraulic motor has a high power/weight ratio which helps considerably to reduce the natural top-heaviness of the vessel, while a high-torque, low-speed motor can eliminate an expensive and large reduction gearbox. The output torque can be very precisely controlled, thereby limiting the power applied to the bucket chain and avoiding overloading with consequent damage to the equipment. Again, variable speed is easily obtainable with a torque characteristic which suits the requirements of the drive.

The drive usually consists of a fixed capacity hydraulic motor driven by a variable capacity pump, which is driven in turn by either an electric motor or a diesel engine, plus the usual ancillary equipment, such as boost pump, servo pump, relief valves, etc. The pump is usually remotely controlled from the bridge, the maximum speed being set to the expected conditions.

A stall feature may be included which causes the pump to reduce capacity in the event of a torque being required which is higher than the available power can provide at the set speed.

When a bucket dredger is being served by hopper barges, some means of diverting the flow of spoil from the buckets to either port or starboard side is necessary. This may be achieved hydraulically using a cylinder of adequate size—controlled from the bridge or from some other remote station—to operate a hinged chute which is designed to close off access to the port chute while still giving clear flow to the starboard chute and vice versa. The overboard chutes on each side may be operated by means of an hydraulic cylinder, or by a winch extending to the working position or retracting when not in use.

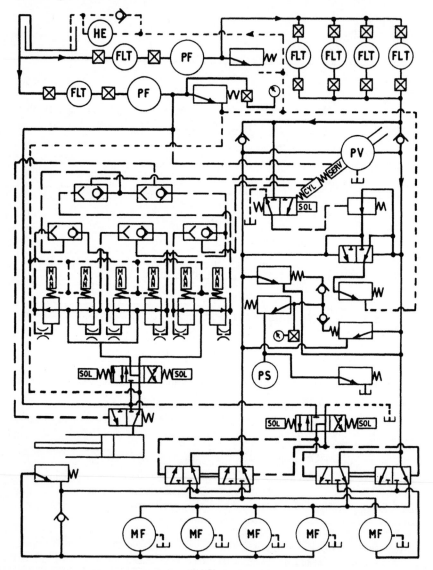

FIG. 66.—*Hydraulic circuit for cutter drive and ladder hoist.*

These auxiliary drives are often run from a ring main supplied by one or more variable capacity pumps which are fitted with stall valves to maintain a constant pressure in the system.

5.9. HATCH COVER ACTUATION

Mechanized hatch cover operation can employ hydraulic circuits driving cylinders, motors or rotary actuators with suitable mechanical linkages or cables to achieve the moving and lifting action.

Once again the problem involves rapid movement under light load, with small movement or holding required with higher forces. Therefore, the most economical circuit can include a small fixed capacity pump operating continuously against a relief valve, with a larger pump to supply flow at a lower pressure. This second pump is unloaded, with the flow passing directly back to tank, when the pressure level demanded exceeds a pre-set value.

Safety precautions must also include check valves to prevent the covers falling under their own weight if hydraulic pressure is lost for any reason during any part of the cycle.

All hatches can be operated from a ring main system with a single power source, and sequencing of individual cover lifting may also be required to achieve the necessary action.

5.10. CARGO LOADING DOORS, LOADING RAMPS AND ELEVATORS

Hydraulic drives for these operations can involve rotary transmissions with high and low speed motors to drive winch drums, or linear drives with cylinders for either direct action or to operate pulley and sheave systems.

Low power hydraulic oil supply is usually involved, with a fixed capacity pump of sufficient capacity to meet the necessary cycle times.

The system design obviously depends upon the overall requirement. In some cases, where multiple operating positions are required, a ring main may be safe, economical and the most convenient but in other circumstances electric cable runs may be preferred with individual miniature power packs sited at each work station.

Systems will often involve sequenced operations with safety overrides, together with operation of cleats or cotters for locking.

5.11. OTHER APPLICATIONS

The descriptions of systems and equipment have had to be confined mainly to situations where standard hydraulic components and techniques are basically involved, and which are tailored to meet the particular problems and requirements of the marine environment. In many cases, the hydraulic power actuation is secondary to the specialist equipment designs provided by marine engineering organizations. In other areas, proprietary hydraulic components are more difficult to utilize and the necessary mechanisms are closely incorporated into the plant or equipment. Such areas as these, *viz.* variable pitch propellors, stabilizers and bow thrusters, are really beyond the scope of this Part, but in practice they also represent important applications of the principles of hydraulic power transmission and control.

6. SOME DEFINITIONS AND EQUATIONS

The following definitions are given for general interest and for help with any further reading.

Power losses due to friction and leakages are ignored, but in practice component and circuit losses can be significant factors in both the design and operation of any system.

6.1. FLOW

The flow (F) delivered from a pump depends directly upon the capacity per revolution (K) and the speed of rotation (N), i.e.

$$F = K \times N \tag{1}$$

6.2. PRESSURE

Pressure is defined as the force per unit area:

$$\text{Pressure } (P) = \frac{\text{Force}}{\text{Area}} \tag{2}$$

6.3. FORCE

From above:

$$\text{Force} = \text{Pressure} \times \text{Area} \tag{3}$$

6.4. TORQUE

The following equations can be shown to be true by detailed analysis of any pump geometry to find the swept volume and the out of balance pressure loads which produce turning moments within the mechanism:

$$\text{Torque} \, (T) = k_1 K \cdot P \tag{4}$$

where k_1 is a numerical constant depending upon the system of units used,

K = Pump capacity,

P = Pump pressure rise (the difference between inlet and outlet pressure).

6.5. POWER

$$\text{Mechanical horsepower} = k_2 N . T \qquad (5)$$

and by substitution of (1) and (4) in (5):

$$\text{Metric horsepower} = k_2(k_1 K . P)\frac{F}{K}$$

$$= k_3 F . P$$

where k_2 and k_3 = numerical constants.

6.6. SOME PRACTICAL RELATIONSHIPS

$$\text{Hydraulic Horsepower} = \frac{\text{Flow (gal/min)} \times \text{Pressure (lbf/in}^2)}{1430}$$

$$\text{Metric Horsepower} = \frac{\text{Flow (l/min)} \times \text{Pressure (bar)}}{448} \times 1 \cdot 014$$

$$\text{Power (kW)} = \frac{\text{Flow (l/min)} \times \text{Pressure (bar)}}{600}$$

Motor Output Torque (lbf ft)

$$= \frac{\text{Capacity (in}^3/\text{rev)} \times \text{Pressure (lbf/in}^2)}{75 \cdot 4} \times \text{Efficiency Factor}$$

Motor Output Torque (kpm)

$$= \frac{\text{Capacity (cm}^3/\text{rev)} \times \text{Pressure (bar)}}{616 \cdot 8} \times \text{Efficiency Factor}$$

Motor Output Torque (Nm)

$$= \frac{\text{Capacity (cm}^3/\text{rev)} \times \text{Pressure (bar)}}{62 \cdot 9} \times \text{Efficiency Factor.}$$

NOTES